W9-CYU-466

HUNGRY

One Woman's Battle with and
Victory over Anorexia and Bulimia

JESSICA Edwards SKINNER

HUNGRY

HUNGRY

ONE WOMAN'S BATTLE
WITH AND VICTORY OVER
ANOREXIA AND BULIMIA

JESSICA EDWARDS SKINNER

Library of Congress Control Number: 2009910593

ISBN: 978-0-578-03975-6

A Burning One Books publication
www.burningonebooks.com

Closer
Words and Music by John Mark McMillan
(c) 2005 Integrity Media, Inc., 1000 Cody Road, Mobile, AL 36695
All Rights Reserved International Copyright Secured   Used by Permission
Reprinted by permission of Hal Leonard Coporation

Cover design by Amber Wong
crazylovegraphics.com
Flower photograph by Ed Brown
www.flickr.com/photos/sojourner-ed/
Book layout by Selfpublishing.com

Printed in the United States of America

CONTENTS

I dedicate this book to you, the reader.
May you find the freedom and love your heart has been longing for.
And to my King Jesus, the reason for my being.
May your Spirit be with all who read this book.

ACKNOWLEDGEMENTS

I want to thank everyone who has helped me on my road to recovery.

To my husband, Jesse—my best friend and biggest fan. Thank you for fighting for my freedom, and for loving me as Christ loves the church. Your love and grace overwhelm me. More than anyone, you have demonstrated to me how to persistently fight the enemy's lies and receive this amazing love and vast inheritance that our Daddy God has lavished on us. You are one of the greatest gifts God has ever given me.

To my parents. You have seen my journey from the beginning. Thank you for never giving up on me. Your prayers have led me home. Your forgiveness, unconditional love, and constant encouragement have blessed me beyond words. I am so honored to call you Mom and Dad.

To my brother, James. Thanks for your love and humor. I love that I can always count on you for a good laugh.

To my extended family. Even though you weren't able to always be there through the healing, your prayers and loving phone calls always spurred me on to take a hold of my freedom.

Thank you to my mom's faithful prayer group. You move mountains with your faith.

And thank you to all of my friends and mentors both past and present. I need each and every one of you. Special thanks to Jim and Eli Munroe who helped lead me back into Daddy's arms. Thank you for getting me on my feet in the first months of my journey. And to Leah—thanks for persistently pouring into me, for helping me to see my true identity as God's daughter, and for always being just a phone call away. Thanks to all of you for being my friend, even when I was the most difficult to love.

I also want to thank my counselors, Amy and Rebecca. Thank you for helping me dig up the lies and cut them off at the roots. You showed me that I can truly live and eat without fear.

And thank you to all the girls at the Breaking Free group. Thank you for your vulnerability, for your bravery in fighting the lies, and for helping me know that I was never alone.

I also want to give special thanks to all of you who took the time to edit my first drafts—my parents, my mom-in-law, Diane, and Margaret Reed. Thanks for your encouragement and critical feedback. Amy Weaver—thank you for being my biggest cheerleader ever! And Sarah Michaelis—in the early days of this book's development, your praise always helped me realize I was born to write.

Special thanks to Marcia Ford for doing the final edit.

And thanks to Jeff and Amber Wong who generously sacrificed their time to do all of my graphic design and headshots.

I wish I wasn't here, writing things I wish you never knew.
But this is where the healing starts.
This book is for you.

INTRODUCTION

I used to think I belonged in a mental institution. Well, actually, I just wanted to be in one. The thought of being strapped down rang heavenly in my head. O, what bliss it would be to live in a mental institution—scheduled meals, no responsibility, people fixing you, nurturing you . . . keeping you from *you*. I would imagine myself in a bed, being brought meals in healthy, small proportions. No grocery stores to haunt me. No difficult choices to make. I'd be analyzed, figured out—problems solved. Then maybe that voice would shut up. Man, can you hear that? Shut up! You hear me, voice? I'm sick of you. Shuuut uuuuup!

I hear this voice, you see. Well, it's quieter now, but I used to hear it all the time, and a lot louder. It told me to do things I didn't want to do. It told me I was crazy. And I agreed. Its voice became mine. "Jessica, you're crazy." I'd say it out loud. "Dang it! What are you doing? You're crazy!"

I'd think, *Can't someone just check me in? I need a doctor. O, God, I need someone to take care of me! I can't do this!*

I did things I thought no one else did. I hid. I'd lock the door and stuff obscenely large quantities of food into my mouth. Then puke it all back up.

It didn't make sense. But I couldn't stop. I was crazy.

I didn't think I was crazy at first. At first I thought I had discovered the best diet ever. Overeat? No problem. Now you can binge without losing the thinness you achieved through anorexia. Just get rid of the extra calories by shoving your fingers down your throat until all your worries come rushing out of your body and into the toilet. I thought it was a phase. But it got worse. Then when I wanted to stop, I was powerless to change. But the puking part isn't nearly the half of it.

I want to tell you a story about my life. I want to share pieces of myself, because what happened to me happens to you. Life happens. Lies happen. Mistakes happen. And if you don't fix them, or learn from them, death is slow, and you'll never be able to live in the light of the present.

You are not alone.

I wrote this book because it's not about me. This life, this journey that we're all on, is about a family of people living toward restoration and freedom. It's about becoming who we were created to be through the resurrection power for Jesus. There's power in my testimony, and by reading it, you get to grab hold of that freedom.

I used to think I belonged in a mental institution. I was wrong. The truth? I believed the lie—the lie that there was no hope, no way out. I wanted someone else to fix me, someone else to solve my problems, someone else to hold me down and keep me from myself. I screamed for God to take it away. And when God Himself didn't fix me right away, I wondered why. But then I learned how He loved me. How He loved me so much that He stood by me as I struggled, watched as I fell and cried and got up, and fell and cried and got up again. He knew a Band-Aid would never work. The pain it must have caused Him!

But it was love that let me scream and scratch my way through an intense healing process. He wanted me to go deeper—to recover my heart. And He was my biggest fan, tireless, never angry, and always wanting me.

Of course, I didn't just wake up one day and decide to be in this battle—to be fighting anorexia or bulimia, fighting thoughts, fighting for my identity. I also never thought I would be here—writing things I wish you never had to know. Author Henri Nouwen once said, "Like Jesus, he who proclaims liberation is called not only to care for his own wounds and the wounds of others, but also to make his wounds into a major source of his healing power." So I have to write now while I'm still wrapping my wounds. And you can watch.

PART I

MY STORY

As we grow, our experiences and the way we interpret the world shape our view of identity. We either perceive ourselves from the enemy's perspective or from God's perspective. As a result, we either react out of fear or live from freedom.

Travel back with me to the places where I believed the enemy and the lies were planted. I want you to see how, if gone unchecked, these lies grow roots of fear. It was these fears that later resulted in two very destructive coping mechanisms: anorexia and bulimia.

CHAPTER 1

WE NEED EACH OTHER

My emotions were blank before all this:

"How do you feel?"
"I dunno."
"What are you thinking about?"
"Ummm, nothing."

I could cry when Bambi's mom died, but when it came to my own human pain, there was nothing. I had no idea how I felt. And I had no idea how I felt when I made myself throw up. I just did it. Like routine.

I didn't know me. Outside there were jokes and laughter and clever remarks. But inside there was only the numbness. My friendships did not run deep. When I came back to God, I came back to life in most areas but one. The place I was most afraid to face: control over food. I tricked myself into thinking it wasn't such a big deal. "I only make myself throw up every once in awhile," the lies would say.

I remember thinking there was a monster living inside me. It wasn't me, but it would act like me all the time. Born of a fear that I would never be loved, it was ugly, and it was smart. It used the one thing it knew I had to use every day and turned it into a weapon against me: food.

I tried hard to make it shut up, but it would start raging to get out. Until it was satisfied, I'd keep cool in public quite well. Remain detached. Smile and think, *OK, don't look at me. Yep, everything's great here, no secrets, just buying some ice cream and cookies, and soda, and cake, and garlic bread like any other normal person.* Dark secrets stay safer if your eyes never meet anyone else's.

I looked normal on the outside, but inside my mind was raging. Focused on one thing and one thing alone: feed the monster. Behind closed doors the chains would fall. The thing was loose, and I'd let it run. I see my hands, and they don't look like mine. I devour the food, all the food, until it hurts, and all the while I think, *I'm crazy. Dang it! I'm crazy! What am I doing? Just stop it!* But I can't. And that's scary. And I'm the only one alive until it's over.

Reason for Change

Unless you get angry, you'll never change. Unless you have a reason to change, to stop making yourself throw up, to stop beating yourself up about a few too many calories, to stop comparing yourself to everyone who crosses your path, to stop wasting your life at the gym—if you don't have a reason to stop all these things, you'll never do anything about it.

In my journey to recovery I've found several reasons to change. First, I could tell you about the media, how angry I am that they spend billions of dollars every year just to make us feel like crap—to make us feel so dissatisfied with ourselves that we go out and buy their stuff.

Or I could tell you about the physical dangers, the most notable being cardiac arrest or heart attack. The vomiting and laxative abuse can also cause chronic illnesses affecting your heart, liver, gastrointestinal tract, or neurological functions. Scarier, an esophageal rupture could occur even the first time you throw up. This could kill you. Psychologically, there is depression.

But because we are invincible, these aren't enough reasons to stop doing what we are doing. So I want to take you a little deeper. Why do we do what we do?

Am I Beautiful?

Most women want to know, *Am I beautiful? Do I possess something that's worthy of being sought after, known, seen, protected, and delighted in? Am I beautiful?*

Why do we long to hear that somebody likes us or thinks we're pretty or funny or interesting? Why do we develop ways to seduce the opposite sex? We don't really want sex. We just want to be desired. To know we're beautiful.

Beauty these days has been cheapened and reduced to Photoshop and vain pursuits. And so time and time again, we take our heart's question to the wrong places: to guys, to magazines, to TV shows, and even to our friends. We compare ourselves, scold ourselves, stare in the mirror, and curse ourselves. The answers we receive are devastating: "No, you're not enough. And you're too much at the same time. You're not small enough, smart enough, fashionable enough, or funny enough. But you're too loud, too quiet, too careful, too curt, too fat, too dorky, and way too complicated for anyone to ever want to get close to."

So we shut up, adjust to what *they* want. We hide our passions, opinions, and desires, and replace them with the desires the world tells us to have: perfect thighs, stomachs, and butts, perfect homes and outfits, perfect guys wanting us. We should play hard to get but not be a prude. And if we manage to do all these things, we should be happy, right? So why are so many of us crying when nobody's looking? Or maybe it's just that you're too numb to have any emotion at all.

The Most Important Reason for Change

Bulimia, or any type of body-image obsession, is a trap. You may not make yourself throw up, but you spend hours at the gym, looking in the mirror, or obsessing over what you have or haven't eaten. Bondage. It causes us to become so focused on ourselves that we have no way of being close to people. We are too busy hiding, thinking about food, the number on the scale, or how many calories we've eaten to ever be present.

In recovery, I've found that the biggest reason to fight the lies is this: to have intimacy with a God who loves me and to share the depths of who I am with my family and friends. To love completely and to be completely loved—to be fully alive and to bring life to a dying world.

What's the most important thing in your life? You may say, "Being a good person." But I would guess that what you really want are deep relationships, intimacy with a God who often feels distant, and closeness with people who love you.

How can we be surrounded by so many people and feel so alone? We are hiding. We've isolated ourselves behind protective walls of shame and unforgiveness without realizing it. We are left with an unquenchable loneliness.

What Made Me Fight?

So what made me fight anorexia and bulimia? God changing my heart. God helping me realize how isolated I had become inside the disorder. I was hiding behind the lies, the stuffed anxiety, and the fear of being seen and rejected. And

God helped me see how I didn't have control of the disorder. It had control of me.

The healing had to start in my heart and mind because willpower wasn't working. Willpower did not carry the transforming power I needed to resist the barrage of negative thoughts. I'd be prodding and poking at my skin, trying on a zillion outfits—in need of a drink to feel confident. I was deceived. Having a perfect body was a very false sense of security.

I was ashamed. I realized how often I had to lie to keep my secret safe and that during all these episodes I was creating a deep chasm between the rest of the world and me. I knew I wanted deep friendships, but I didn't know how to get them.

I finally realized I didn't want to live in this trap forever. I would imagine myself a mother, putting down my toddler to hide behind a locked door and throw up as she cried outside. I didn't want that. I didn't want to pass my insecurities on to my daughters. And I still don't. I fight because I don't want my four-year-old looking in the mirror and thinking she is fat. I fight because I want to share a love with my husband that goes deeper than physical pleasure. I want to be comfortable in my own skin so he can see me—really see me. I want him to be able to look into my eyes and find that there's a depth worth exploring. And I want to be able to love him, to breathe life into him, instead of using him just so I can feel loved.

I've realized that who I am is not just what you see. My body is not who I am. There is a soul and a spirit in here. There is a character and personality in here that were especially designed to be alive today. And by being bulimic, I'm killing that girl. I'm becoming numb and slowly dying.

We Need Each Other

We need each other. I am writing because I care about you. I know the struggle of being a woman and wanting to be wanted so much that you would live on a permanent no-carb, fat-free diet or shove your fingers down your throat just to feel beautiful.

So I've decided to be open, to unfold my story, no details spared. Nobody wants to read a book called *Assorted Spiritual Tidbits: Both Impersonal and Generic*. People want juicy gossip. Something they can gasp at. Why? Because we all have a desire to know one another.

Our hunger for gossip is really just a twisted desire for closeness. There's a poverty of intimacy that plagues our country. Technology, business, shame, the desire to be perfect—they have all robbed us of true friendships. So starting now, I'll let you feel close. I don't really want to. But you need me. Just like I need you. Let me take you back to the beginning.

CHAPTER 2

I HATE PEER PRESSURE: IT'S SO CLICHÉ

ELEMENTARY school lessons on peer pressure always had me visualizing unrealistic things. Like the creepy guy in the dark alley tempting me with a cigarette. I would never fall for that. The D.A.R.E. videos were full of them. And I hated talks on peer pressure because they were always given by adults who didn't know anything.

I was a good girl. I lived above it all, born and raised in beautiful Newport Beach, California, in the safety of a Christian home. I became a Christian when I was seven and never wanted to do bad things like watch R-rated movies or kiss boys. Inside this bubble, the picture I had of the world was black and white. The black was all the scary, evil stuff, like drinking and smoking and lust and things I would never want to touch. The white was all the well-mannered stuff we learned at Mariners Christian School.

We were all warned that we would face peer pressure—the truth is we were born into a battle—but the visions of the dark alley or people laughing and trying to get me to drink never looked tempting. Inside my head they just looked stupid.

Boys

Then somewhere around junior high, the bubble was no longer safe. Youth group meetings became nervous times when attention wavered between the pastor and the hope that the cute guy liked me. I desperately wanted to be cool. My friends and I gawked at magazines, and our lockers were filled with pictures of cute boy stars. We talked about who we had crushes on and judged each other's

21

taste. I wasn't really interested, but if I didn't have crushes that meant there was something wrong with me. I didn't want anything to be wrong with me.

We weren't drinking or having sex (I couldn't even say that word back then), but we were compromising without knowing it. The enemy was lying to us, and we believed him. We invited him right in through our TVs, magazines, and CDs. We weren't living in the kingdom. We were living under the government of the evil one. He deceived us into being religious, into believing that as long as we had our Bibles and church and Christian school and followed the Ten Commandments, we were fine.

This was peer pressure.

Competition and Agreement

And there was competition. Junior high is a breeding ground for competitive thoughts. Who has the biggest boobs, the cutest clothes, and the best body? What we were really asking was, *How do I compare? How do I measure up? Am I OK?* I didn't realize I was making comparisons all the time or how illogical those comparisons were. But back then it didn't matter. I just wanted to be wanted. *This* was peer pressure. It came as a feeling, unseen and unheard.

Competition is the enemy's favorite wrecking ball. It's his way of getting us to agree with him. He knows agreements are powerful because they are God's way of doing things. Matthew 18:19-21 says, "If two of you on earth agree about anything you ask for, it will be done for you by my Father in heaven." Our lives are composed of agreements, good or bad. For instance, if I agree that the University of San Diego is the best school to go to, I will go there. In the same way, if I agree that so-and-so is not cool, I will treat her differently.

The enemy is not a creator and cannot create anything new, but he can take what God has created and pervert it for his purposes.

If you're thinking negative thoughts about someone, you've just agreed with the enemy. Your agreement is strong, and you can be sure that the person you're thinking about is feeling the weight of your agreement.

The best way to resolve this is to do what you least want to: declare blessings over him or her. You can reverse the attack of the enemy by standing in agreement with your friend instead of competing with her in your thoughts. Not only will you find yourself loving that person, but you'll also begin to feel better about yourself. The tongue has the power of life and death. We can either kill each other with all the competitive things we do, like gossiping and comparing, or we can give life by building each other up.

Agreements with Yourself

The power of agreement transfers to the self as well. I was good at agreeing with the enemy about my body and my worth. But I've learned that I can't love people if I hate myself.

I had to take my thoughts captive.

Instead of agreeing with the enemy, I had to agree with what God says about me. He doesn't say, "She's prettier than you" or "Your stomach is looking bigger today." He says, "You are fearfully and wonderfully made. I handcrafted you with great care, and I take delight in every detail. You are beautiful!"

Usually when we're attacked, it's hard to believe this truth, but we need to speak it over our lives regardless. Don't go signing any contracts with the enemy. We need to stand up for one another, not compete with one another. I wish I had known this back then. Maybe I wouldn't have been so insecure.

Compromise and Rejection

I carried these insecurities into public high school. Corona del Mar High was a fashion show. Not good for an insecure Christian girl. As my unnoticed comparisons continued, I began negotiating my morality—little things like not finding Christian friends. I wanted to be cool. I compromised whenever I feared rejection. At first I felt like Lot, tormented in my soul by the foulness that surrounded me. The unnecessary use of the "F" word bothered me, but I got used to it. Soon I was dating a guy who wanted to kiss in a way I didn't. But it was nice to be wanted, and I didn't want him rejecting me like the last guy did.

The last guy had been my first boyfriend. I was fifteen. I had never been kissed, so it was awkward when he tried to kiss me. He was a junior, and I'm sure he had kissed plenty of girls. I wasn't about to make a fool of myself, so I played shy and pulled away. He told me he loved me. I didn't say it back. I wanted it to be right. But he was a Christian, too, so I thought I was just being a prude.

Finally, while on a family vacation in Hawaii, I gave in and wrote him a postcard telling him I loved him. He broke up with me the day I returned. I was mortified. I had dangled my heart in front of him, but instead of coddling it, he tried to tear it in two. And he would have made away with half of my heart had

I not made a vow that day. I vowed to never love again. Never again would I let someone hurt me. Never again would I be made to look like a fool. I swallowed the pain, toughened up, and tossed the dried roses in the trash.

That one vow, which was nothing more than a subtle thought, has caused me a lot of pain. Instead of forgiving him, I let that one little vow create a callous around the piece of my heart called vulnerable. Love is vulnerable. It's alive and pouring out of a spirit full of life. I killed a piece of myself that day.

Have you ever made a vow like this?

Think back into your childhood, to the times you've been hurt. What did you promise yourself to do or never do again in order to protect yourself? Once you've found the agreement, renounce it. You could say something like, "Lord, forgive me for making the vow that I will never love again. I break the power of that agreement and declare that I *will* give and receive love—Your love. I am not an island. I need people, and I desire to learn how to be vulnerable in the ways you desire for me."

As high school continued, so did my desire to not be the naïve Christian. I became the designated driver, saying things like, "I don't do what they do, Mom. They're just my friends; stop judging them." My poor little spirit wanted to be wanted so badly that I got as close to the edge as I could without breaking "the rules." I was angry at my parents for not letting me do certain things. I was so afraid of rejection, of missing out. *This* was peer pressure. The unrest in my soul was heavy.

God, Where Is Your Power?

I wanted to be known, but I also wanted to be close to God. Why couldn't I just have both? I had tons of friends, but none felt close. I tried to encourage myself with the knowledge that God was there. But even though I knew there was a God, He didn't feel close. I had no idea how to access His tangible love. Knowing He was there wasn't enough. I needed more. I needed to feel Him. What good is a relationship without experience?

And what happened to all those miracles Jesus did? Is all this faith for nothing? Why do people in the world have more fun than people in church? Why don't people want to hear about Jesus? What happened to the book of Acts? Where is the *power*?

When the church didn't answer, I faded into the background. I didn't know how to get closer to God. I didn't spend mornings or nights reading my Bible and singing to Him in my room as I do now. I was only memorizing His Word because I thought I had to, not because I loved poring over the pages with Him. Church became routine, and it looked as if everyone else was living a mundane Christian life, too. Just floating along. *This* was peer pressure.

My church friends and I never talked about amazing encounters we had with God because we never had any, except maybe on mission trips to Mexico. We knew all the right answers in church. But the rest of the time, we searched for ways to entertain ourselves with movies and youth group scavenger hunts. We talked about boys and movies and teachers we didn't like and . . . gossip. Good, hearty Christian gossip, like ragging on the immorality of others. And most of the time, I hated it. I didn't want to talk about that stuff. I always felt out of the loop anyway. But the older I got, the desire to look a certain way became stronger. Oh, that subtle peer pressure.

I wasn't open about my faith because it wasn't consistently real. I would pray, but life wasn't pouring out of me. I didn't know how to be filled on a daily basis. In the end, Mom was right. People are like sponges, and we become who we hang out with.

What does all of this have to do with eating disorders? Plenty. Eating disorders don't just happen. They're a result of years of wrong thinking, years of listening to the enemy's lies, years of unforgiveness toward people who hurt you. They come from a lack of intimacy with the Father.

Ticket into Heaven

Have you ever noticed how "I just don't want to" or "I don't drink because I'm a Christian" doesn't explain much? Especially not to a beer-and-testosterone-filled football player whose only goal in life is to make sure everyone is "having a good time."

I finally cracked at a Jimmy Buffett concert. It was 1999, my junior year of high school. I had been the outsider long enough. Deep down, I was mad at God for not proving Himself more powerful. I lost trust in Him and thought He was withholding the real fun from me. He said obedience would bring life, but in my experience, it had only brought rejection.

Everything religion had taught me was that God was the cosmic *no*. Fun? No, you can't have that. Stay out past ten? No, only bad things happen that late.

Sex? No, that's bad. Movies? No, they're evil. Unfortunately, a segment of the church went through a period when people were taught to isolate themselves from the big bad world. But that doesn't bring the freedom God intended for us to live in. It only leaves us on the defensive, managing our sins instead of overcoming them.

We were made to overcome temptation to such a degree that we don't even pay it any mind, because we're too busy bringing life and setting others free. But seeing God as the "cosmic no" leaves us weak and ashamed, wanting to rebel instead of getting closer. It causes us to live in fear: fear of messing up, fear of the world, fear of God being mad at us and punishing us or just ignoring us, fear of being rejected.

So at the Buffett concert, I decided to have a beer in the parking lot before I went in. Some of the girls from my volleyball team were there and were quick to assist me. As I rowdily stumbled into the concert, I was greeted with, "Edwards! Are you drunk? Wow, Edwards is wasted!" They embraced me like never before. The turmoil in my wounded soul had ended. Or so I thought. The peer pressure that I thought I was so above was now radically changing the course of my life.

I knew that what I was doing was wrong, but it was fun. And hey, if God is so forgiving, and I already had my ticket into heaven, then I could just do what I wanted and go to Him for forgiveness when I was good and ready, right? I'm not hurting anyone. I'm a genuinely good person. Why miss out on the best years of my life?

There's a reason why the Word says, "Taste and see that the Lord is good" (Psalm 34:8). A relationship with God involves all of our senses. And when we experience and encounter God's love, the lesser pleasures of the world look, feel, and taste like poison in comparison. There is nothing that compares with the superior pleasures of our King. He's not the cosmic *no*. He's the cosmic *yes*.

But back then, those wonderful joys that the Bible talked about seemed unattainable. They were reserved for the super religious. And from what I had experienced as a Christian (rejection, missing out, rules, and songs without encounters), I knew I didn't want to be super religious. Bible verses that spoke of the peace and joy I would get if I was obedient seemed unrealistic—grin and bear it, soon you'll be in heaven. So, I fooled the system by doing what I thought was bringing me joy on earth. Then at the end, I could get into heaven, because I had my ticket.

Eternal Life

But we don't have to wait to "get into heaven" to experience perfect joy. The Bible doesn't even mention this notion of "going to heaven." It does say things like, "entering the kingdom of heaven," "inheriting the kingdom," and "the kingdom of heaven is at hand." The kingdom is within reach, right here, right now.

The Bible also does not say that if you believe in God you will go to heaven. Seriously. You can check it out. It does mention, however, that you will inherit eternal life. John 17:3 says, "Now this is eternal life: that they may know you, the only true God, and Jesus Christ, whom you have sent." The word *know* in that context means knowing as a result of experience and intimacy. Knowing what's on His heart, knowing that He thinks you're amazing and He can't get enough of you, knowing how He moves and speaks, recognizing His voice. Hanging out with Him like best friends—like husband and wife.

When we do that, we manifest His kingdom, His way of doing things, right where we are. When we know who He is, we learn who we are and how we're supposed to operate.

Knowing God

Someone once told me that if I knew the Lord and how much I was worth in His eyes, I wouldn't harm my body. Doing things like being bulimic is simply a result of not knowing Him. "No one who continues to sin has either seen Him or known Him" (1 John 3:6). These words are not to bring us shame or condemnation but to show why we do the things we do, why we feel discontent with God: we don't truly *know* Him.

If we truly knew Him, we would know that He only has plans to bring us delight and fulfillment. We would know the feeling of being close to Him, and it would feel too good for us to ever desire compromise. We would hate sin, not because the Bible says it's bad, but because it hurts to be apart from our Father. We would hate to hurt His tender heart.

Like many of you, I knew God existed, but I didn't know what stirred His heart. I knew plenty about Him, but I didn't know what He was thinking about. I may have sung the songs in church, but the words just floated into the air. I wasn't encountering Him and His love.

But there is no condemnation in Christ Jesus. If you're struggling with an eating disorder, you don't need any more reasons to beat up on yourself than you already have. Please don't tell yourself what an awful person you are.

God wants to give you a vast inheritance, overflowing joy, visions, encounters with Him and His angels, ecstasy, peace, creativity, supernatural ideas and cures for cancer, ideas for worship songs that break the chains off of a dying generation . . . *power!*

Living in His kingdom is not about what you can't do. It's about what you *can* do. Don't make the same mistake I did. I sold my inheritance for years of compromise, drinking, guys, and ultimately depression. I thought I was just a sinner, so I acted like one. But the Bible says I'm a saint! Yes, I may mess up, but because of Jesus, it's not my nature anymore (see Romans 6–8). I am royalty.

The Fateful Decision

God will forgive me when I'm good and ready, I thought as my junior year in high school wore on. *I'm not as bad as so-and-so.* These were the thoughts that kept me trapped. I couldn't see that a true relationship with God wasn't about missing out on fun. Instead, experiencing Him is the closest to ecstasy a human can get. He's the one who made us. He should know what we like.

As I proceeded to live in this delusional state, soon the drinking wasn't enough. I wanted to be skinny. *This* was that elusive peer pressure again. I remember complaining to my mom about feeling fat. I had made casual comments here and there since I was younger—I was listening to the enemy's lies. But of course, being a good mom, she said I looked fine and promised to tell me if she thought I should lose weight.

I had played high school and club volleyball and soccer most of my life, so I never had to watch what I ate. I didn't realize that food was a comfort for me, bringing me satisfaction when I felt restless or hurt by the world. One night before dinner, I was coming out of the pantry with another study snack, and my mom asked, "How many snacks have you eaten?" Immediately my mind translated that into, *See, even Mom thinks I'm fat. I knew it. I'm fat!*

I'm sure she just didn't want me to spoil my dinner.

Unforgiveness and Self-preservation Lead to Sin

But it was too late. The liar was loud: *Fat equals rejection,* and I took the bait. I didn't know God's voice, so I couldn't hear the truth. I tried eating healthy food and started running, but I wanted results fast. *I'll show them,* I thought. I had been hurt by the kids at school who made me feel like an outsider (mainly nonverbally), hurt by my parents in ways I did not recognize, and hurt by God for not proving Himself stronger. Instead of forgiving and clinging to truth, I believed the lies and let unforgiveness brew a bitterness that wanted revenge. I wanted so desperately to be seen and heard, to be delighted in, to stop the feelings of rejection.

Did I recognize this at the time? No, but God has shown me the strongholds that unforgiveness produces. When we don't forgive those who hurt us, we end up wanting to hurt them back. My sin manifested in negative thoughts toward others to make myself feel better, it manifested in jealousy and self-pity, and it manifested in rebellion and an attitude of "I'll show them!"

I felt justified because I was the victim. I had to protect myself. Sadly, the walls not only protected me but also prevented me from receiving love.

At seventeen, I had decided that self-preservation meant getting skinny and beautiful. I knew I could make the numbers on my new scale drop faster if I stopped eating. How long could I go without eating? I have no idea why I chose to do that. I didn't know anyone who was doing it. It was my own secret resolution. And it wasn't just my mother's comment. The liar had been planting lies in my head since the day I arrived on this earth. Her comment was simply twisted to fulfill his master plan to steal from me, to kill me, and to ultimately destroy me.

My New Favorite Hobby

I had gotten a scale for Christmas and started using it aggressively. Watching the numbers drop became my new favorite hobby. And people said I was looking great. This positive reinforcement was peer pressure, again posing as something other than what I had imagined. *I lost fifteen pounds on the "No Food Diet"!*

Nobody knew how I was doing it at first. I lied all the time, saying I already ate, or saying I wanted a protein shake for dinner and then flushing it down the toilet upstairs. I would come home for lunch and pick at a protein snack bar, eating it one tiny bite at a time, and enjoying every bit of control. I wouldn't even drink a whole Diet Snapple because it would fill my stomach. Feeling full equaled fat.

At first I didn't mind the isolation, because I was achieving something. The numbers were dropping. I weighed myself when I woke up and after I went to the bathroom and after I took a shower and when I got home and after I ate and when I went to bed. On good days the digital numbers dropped a few decimals through the course of the day. But I always had to weigh at least two-tenths of a pound less the next morning than the morning before. This meant I was doing a good job.

My Other Favorite Hobby

There was another object that suddenly gained magnetic power: the mirror. I couldn't stay away. I would pick up the handheld and analyze my naked body from all angles: sitting, standing, lying on my back, lying on my stomach, lying on my side. I would pull at my skin, prodding and poking, measuring with my eyes. I lost hours doing this.

For the first time, I felt good in a bathing suit. I started dating a popular football player. *This* was peer pressure: *You're doing great, Jess. Now all the hot guys think you're hot.*

I went to Australia to do dolphin research with Earthwatch and didn't eat there either. And I remember one of the women on the team saying she noticed I didn't eat much, but I was shocked. I thought I was eating a lot! At every group dinner, I had to sit there and put some food on my plate, food that was definitely not allowed, like stir-fried chicken and rice. "What?" I said. "No. I eat a lot!"

I finally understood what Cher in *Clueless* meant when she said, "I feel like a total heifer. I had like five peanut M&M's and three pieces of licorice." No kidding. I would never eat one M&M, let alone five. Those things were like giant pieces of lard that if placed in my mouth would instantly explode under my skin, forming unsightly rolls in the arms, thighs, and butt region.

Many pictures from that time show my emaciated stomach. In other shots, I just looked like a normal seventeen-year-old. I wasn't too obvious.

But when I returned for my senior year, people were stunned. Some didn't recognize me. They started to talk. I thought they were jealous. I started going to more parties, getting more attention, and hanging out with the more popular group of kids. This sounds like a bad high school movie, but it was true. It felt great. But I was kidding myself. These people weren't my friends. I kept going to the parties because I wanted to be in on life. And I unknowingly hurt a lot of people in the process. I had no idea how selfish I had become. I was totally broken inside, and this was the only way I knew how to fix it: Stop sulking and jump in.

Peer pressure came in many forms, but it was never the guy in the dark alley or the friends chanting, "Drink! Drink! Drink!" No one ever forced me to do anything. But peer pressure is the reason why we don't wear pajamas to high school unless everyone else is doing it. It's the reason friends often end up looking the same. It's the subtle guidelines our culture and age groups give us through the images of everyday life. And it's the positive reinforcement when we comply with *their* ways.

How ironic that in our attempts at being unique, we end up more conformist than we could have ever imagined.

CHAPTER 3

DENIAL: I AM NOT ANOREXIC

I remember my brother mentioning anorexia one night at the dinner table. "What? I am not anorexic. Anorexics are people who are skin and bone. I definitely have fat on my body. They're people who don't eat anything. I eat a lot," I said.

Sure I did. I ate only food I knew the calorie content of. It had to have a label. That meant no meat. I ate vegetables and things like a half cup of kidney beans. Or a half cup of cottage cheese—anything with zero fat grams, anything I could measure. Fat was the enemy. I remember scoffing at a Nutri-Grain bar for claiming itself healthy. "Healthy? You're lying to America. These things have three whole grams of fat in them!"

Anorexia and bulimia are an indication that the enemy has messed with your brain. I had no idea that what I was doing was unhealthy or wrong, and I truly believed that I was nowhere near being anorexic. Nothing I had experienced told me that. The compliments and acceptance I received in the beginning canceled the voices of concern that came later. Those voices became the enemy. "They're just jealous or your self-control. They want to take this away from you. They want you to be fat again. You need this to stay pretty and accepted." The liar was loud. His claws were in.

Denial brought many tearful fights with Mom. She started making me weigh myself in front of her, so I would squeeze large, full shampoo bottles between my legs as I stood there in my towel so it would look as if I weighed more than I did. But she didn't know what to do. And the shampoo didn't help.

Denial Must Be Dealt With

Nobody ever knows what to do about people with eating disorders. People are afraid of eating disorders. Most don't even see them until it's too late because you don't have to look as if you have an eating disorder to have one. Most people look like anybody else. When people start suspecting, it's probably already been going on for months, even years, and nobody knows what to do. It's hard for even me to know what to do, and I've been there. But I can give you this advice: Have compassion. There is a terrible lack of compassion concerning eating disorders.

I remember a girl at school grabbing the skin on my stomach, saying, "Eew— gross!" I guess my thinness disgusted her, but I took it as a compliment and left the scene embittered. Comments like that only made me even more stubborn. *Whatever,* I thought. *You're skinny, too. I'm not doing anything wrong. You're just jealous. You don't want me being skinnier than you.* The need for self-preservation would do anything to make it somebody else's fault or problem.

Sure, eating disorders are gross. But they're shameful. That's why they're hidden. And that's why there's denial. Do you have any idea what it's like to come to grips with what you are doing?

Eating disorders are also intolerably selfish. I became so engrossed with myself and my weight and my food and my numbers, numbers, numbers, and how I looked compared to everyone else. I ironically compromised friendships instead of gaining them. It's hard to feel compassion for someone so full of them- selves. And it's easy to get frustrated and think, *Why don't you just eat something, for Christ's sake!*

One time at a Dairy Queen, my friends tried to get me to have a bite of a Blizzard, annoyed and bewildered that I wouldn't give in. And it gave me pleasure to see them eating fattening food while I stayed strong despite their tempting.

That reminds me. I was always pawning off fattening food on everyone. If we had leftovers at my house, I couldn't bear to see that food go to waste, but I would never eat it, so I would invite my friends over for lunch break. I enjoyed knowing the calories were going into them (I fooled them into getting fat), while I maintained control eating a 70-calorie, nonfat yogurt. I would make my brother milkshakes, because it subconsciously made me feel better about myself. It ensured that I was eating fewer calories than he was. It was my unac- knowledged way of getting revenge.

I was also obsessed with the Food Network. I never ate anything that the show hosts cooked, but there was something about watching others getting fat that empowered me. It helped me feel as if I had control while others fell into the trap. Food was always on my mind. I was watching it, making it for someone else, or thinking about what I was going to eat next to stay within my calorie limit.

People usually get frustrated and give up trying to help because the person with the problem will keep pushing them away. Know that somewhere deep inside is a rejected little kid who desperately wants to be free. The worst thing you can do is to ignore the problem or hope someone else is addressing it.

My volleyball coach stopped playing me. Later I learned it was because he thought I was too skinny. It made me so mad and hurt me so much that he never talked to me about it. He watched me killing myself and said nothing. Don't be like him. Suck it up and confront the issue. (I discuss more about how to help someone who is struggling with an eating disorder in the chapter entitled "For Friends and Family" in Part II of this book.)

CHAPTER 4

FROM ANOREXIA TO BULIMIA

"You're Fat" Has a New Solution

HIGH school ended. I never received counseling for anorexia. A master in the art of disguise, I had gained a few pounds to get people off my back. In college at the University of San Diego, nobody knew the pre-eating-disorder Jessica, so they had no idea how unnatural my small frame was. Everyone was skinny. I stopped losing weight but was still maintaining. My constant weigh-ins continued. My food rules didn't change. I had to make sure I never went over a certain number on the scale because if I did, I was fat and I may as well die. I never missed a workout. Numbers filled my head. I was severely bound.

I got good grades, worked out like crazy, joined the Alpha Phi sorority, and partied hard, and when I took a break to breathe, which was rare, I was depressed.

Once while living in Spain my junior, year I was bombarded by an overwhelming sense of worthlessness, as if I was wasting my life. I wrote about my feelings that day, and it was the one journal entry where I actually allowed myself to be real—to feel me. The other entries were laced with choice words about how this was the "effing raddest time of my life." But this one time . . . this one time . . . I wrote how I felt. I knew I should be doing something else with my life. "I should be helping people," I wrote. "How did I get here?" Getting drunk was getting old.

Bigger Than Entertainment

I remember being stoned and looking in the mirror. Staring at my face, I thought, *Who the hell are you?* (Excuse the language.) I pulled on my cheeks and looked into my eyes, hardly recognizing me. I looked dead. Moments of reality would slip in like this to warn me, but I'd be quick to brush them away and return to the party.

Living for entertainment is an inferior way to live. The joy deceives. It never lasts. When we were young, we had a much better concept of living for something bigger than entertainment. Sure, all we did was play games, but to us, they were more than games. We played doctor—I'm a healer. We played house—I'm a nurturer. We climbed trees—I'm a conqueror! We knew without knowing that there were forces in this universe bigger than money (we saw the sky), doors (we walked through without knocking), and stop signs (we went); we lived—much bigger than entertainment.

All of our games were pointing to our purpose. They were prophetic acts, leading the way to our identities as supernatural children. We were made to live for more than parties, concerts, and movies. And by living for the weekend, the next party, the next high, I was living for an inferior purpose. I was killing my true identity. And after I had tasted all of what the world had to offer, I longed for more.

What are *you* living for? Does it fulfill your deepest dreams and desires? Is it motivated out of fear? Does it ever satisfy, or is it like trying to grasp the wind?

The First Time I Purged

Toward the end of my stint in Spain, a group of us girls spent Thanksgiving at a friend's house in Naples, Italy. It was an amazing dinner with lots of food—too much food for a girl with rules. One of the girls had a home video of herself as a professional ballerina. As we watched it, she described how horrible it was to live in the world of ballet and how she used to make herself throw up. Hmmm. I wonder if I could do that.

I went downstairs to the bathroom to try. I closed the door and locked it. It had to be quick. As a rush of thoughts flooded my head, there was one thing that never entered my brain. I didn't think I was being bulimic. I was simply "pulling the trigger"—what any respectable drinker would do if she was expected to make it through a night of drinking. But this wasn't about drinking. It was the food I was concerned with.

I positioned myself over the toilet and stuck two fingers into my mouth. I gagged. Not much success. My eyes watered. Panicked and frustrated, I gave it a few more tries. Still not much coming up, but my eyes burned, the pressure in my sinuses was getting stronger, my heart raced, and at any minute someone could walk by and hear me. I had to go back upstairs.

That was the beginning of a new phase. The lies that played in my head were now manifesting in a new way. "You're fat" had a new solution.

I Am Not Bulimic

I never thought of throwing up as being bulimic. I was simply getting rid of the extra calories. And it was only to be used occasionally—if I messed up. The drinking, smoking, and late-night munchies had made me a horrible anorexic. I was breaking way too many rules. I felt disgusting and looked worse. Of course, I didn't equate this to the partying and numbing of my spirit. I blamed it all on the lack of self-control around food. If I could just get back that control, everything would be good again. Throwing up put me back in the driver's seat.

Denial is the worst enemy of someone with any type of bondage to food. Peer pressure tells you you're fine. Competition tells you they're jealous. Compromise tells you you're a good person and you'll be forgiven when you're good and ready. The liar is loud. His thoughts are yours. *I'm fine. I've got it all under control. Really. It's not so bad. As long as they don't find out, it's not real.* And without some serious intervention, lies will feed lies and rules will breed rules until you are so isolated and trapped inside of your swirling thoughts that you are numb, bound, and dying. The devourer's master plan has been accomplished.

The Blessed Meeting

Still a junior in college and back at home for the holidays, I resolved to get my life back in order. My new diet trick would help. I also decided to sell the bong and stop drinking so much. If I could just get my act together, then I'd be OK.

In the meantime my dad, who is in the business of partnering with philanthropic organizations, wanted me to meet his latest investment: Jim Munroe. Jim was a college campus missionary. Perfect.

"Dad, why do I have to meet him?"

He wanted my take on Jim's ability to relate to college students. I was the most available victim. Reluctant, I met Jim. He shared his story of becoming a Christian, did some magic tricks, which were actually pretty mind-blowing, and told my parents all about his passion to "reach the campus for Christ." I thought the illusion tricks were cool, but since I grew up around Christians my entire life and heard story after story of the addicts who turned Christian, Jim's story was lost on me. I knew what living the Christian life meant: boring churches and boring Christian hangouts like sober bowling and sober game nights. And sitting with my parents always put me on the defensive. I had to keep all my secrets safe inside.

Before parting, we exchanged email addresses. I returned to San Diego for the second semester of my junior year, and Jim went back to Texas.

Powerless Willpower

My time in Spain and run-ins with feeling worthless landed me back in San Diego with the hope of a new resolution. I would lose weight and party less. This should be easy.

But as willpower goes, it didn't last. How was I going to turn down a party in my junior year of college? How was I supposed to stop smoking pot when there was always an opportunity to puff, puff, give? Turning it down was like insulting the almighty marijuana gods. I couldn't risk assaulting the very grounds on which I stood. And not being wasted among a crowd of drunkards was like making a declaration to be left out and totally annoyed all night.

And so a few months later, I still wasn't happy. Bulimia was getting to be very time-consuming. My life really didn't have depth. There was my body, food, the gym, school, and parties. Here I was about to be a senior, and I felt as if my life wasn't going anywhere. Workout, school, party, guys, food, workout, school, party, food, workout, food, workout, food. Workout, workout, workout.

I was good at getting things done, running errands like going to the tanning salon, but I was really just filling my days to avoid depression—to avoid reality. I was trapped. I was lonely. But I didn't slow down enough to ever let myself *feel*.

There's got to be more to life than this.

Bulimia Takes Over

Jim and I had been keeping in touch here and there via email. I lied mostly, telling him religious things like, "I'm praying for you" (yeah right), and "God bless." And I continued with the bulimia. It progressed rapidly from once in awhile to a couple of times a day. I would do weird things like eat large salads and throw up half, measuring the amount with my eyes. Or sometimes I would binge on forbidden food like rice, finally free from the rules of anorexia, only to throw it up moments later. I had a great little system going for me. And I hid it very well.

The episodes continued to get more and more intense; and, in order to maintain appearances, I learned to be more secretive. Let me be specific: In San Diego, during one of our frequent South Mission Beach all-day beachfront keg parties, some friends and I ran over to a little Italian place called Gabiano's for some food. After finishing a sub sandwich—the sandwich I ordered because I knew I could throw it up—I hurried home for a shower. I didn't need a shower. I just needed to throw up. I got into the shower with a big plastic cup and shoved my fingers back and forth into my throat. I must have gagged and threw up about fifteen times. Each time the cup got full, I emptied it into the toilet.

I did this until I was certain that every piece of that sandwich was accounted for. I remember my frantic motions, frantic because I wanted to get it over with quickly, and frantic because the throwing up made my heart race. I was out of breath. The pressure built up in my sinuses and eyes. When it felt as if there were still pieces in my stomach, I guzzled shower water and tried again and again and again. The motion of my hand rubbing against my mouth was forming little cracks in the corners.

When the gagging ceased to yield anything but water, I faced the shower and quickly let the water cleanse my face, hands, all around the tub, the cup. I shakily washed up and made sure no evidence was left. I got out, blew my nose, and avoided my reflection. I washed and dried the cup, hid it back in my room, put drops in my eyes, put my bathing suit back on, fixed my makeup, forced myself to smile, denied what I had just done, and returned to the party.

This was becoming the process every time I ate.

What a waste of life.

It's hard for me to write this, because for years I kept these details safe and private. I am choosing to share them with you, not to focus on the 'how', but to show you the extent of the disorder. It's not some quick-and-easy diet plan. It's not pain-free. It's not simple. It's painful, embarrassing, destructive, shameful, and secretive. It's the reality of a bigger problem inside the minds of many women, and it's a reality whose evidence is being locked behind doors and flushed down toilets.

Despite the denial, I knew it was wrong. Why else would I be hiding?

The Night My Roommates Found Out

The most horrible thing that I could possibly imagine was for someone to find out. But you can only hide for so long.

After devouring a carton of rice one night, I told my roommates to go on ahead to a party without me because I had to make a phone call. Suspicious, one of them stayed behind and said she'd wait for me. Dang it! I frantically tried to convince her not to stay, but I didn't want to be too obvious. I was trapped. I went into the bathroom and tried to be quiet about it by pretending to talk on the phone to my boyfriend. Katie barged in on me, so I quickly turned and sat on the toilet, pretending to cry because my eyes were watering.

"Did you just throw up?" she asked.

"No. I'm just talking to Brett and . . . hold on . . . I'll tell you about it in a minute," I said, blubbering and pushing her out with my head down, hoping my hair and hands would hide any evidence.

I was panicking. *How much did she see? How can I cover my tracks? Think, Jessica.* Once I formulated a good lie, I went to her room and explained that I was crying because I had read Brett one of my poems, and instead of paying attention, he kept talking to his friends in the background. Yes, the lies got pretty detailed. I would do anything to keep my secret safe.

After that, I began throwing up in my room. I'd turn up the music, lock the door and throw up in a big pitcher. I'd then cover it with a towel, wait for the coast to be clear and quickly dump it in the toilet. Talk about bondage.

The denial was thick, but there was a little piece of my heart that still knew there was a God. I am now aware that because people were praying for me, Holy Spirit was hovering around me, wooing me to return to His love—and that little piece of my heart began to push through the walls and cry out for help.

CHAPTER 5

FACING THE TRUTH: MY GOD ENCOUNTER

I don't know what possessed me to be real, but that April of my junior year, 2003, I found myself in the computer lab at USD emailing Jim. This time it was different. Instead of the usual "God bless," I told him the truth—I wasn't living for God. I said I knew God was real, but I didn't want to serve Him yet. I wanted to wait until college was over so I could settle down with a husband and a white picket fence and go back to church.

"Call me," he wrote.

I don't remember the conversations well, but I do remember my heart racing as I faced the truth that I was lost and needed God *now*. But it was impossible. I didn't want to be a hypocrite and go to church while living in complete debauchery. So choosing God meant all or nothing. And it didn't make sense. It couldn't be possible. I could not comprehend how I could possibly drop this life and get a new one. I didn't know how to live any other way. It scared me to death. What about my friends? How would I explain it? Will I have to dump them, too? Are there cool Christians out there who actually live this thing for real? There's no way! I can't do this. I would have to start all over. And then it hit me. You know that religious term everyone throws around: "born again"? Well, it actually means something, and it happened to me.

Journal Entry from April 30, 2003:

The Revelation

Overwhelmed, I broke down. Over what? I felt so weak, so unsure, so confused. My head was swirling. Swirling for way too long. What am I doing? Where am I going? Summer classes? Bio major? What am I doing with my life? Too many things . . . overwhelmed, I broke down. I ran past the keg and into my room. I threw my arms into the air and cried out to You, "Oh, God I need You! I'm so lost! I need You! Oh God, oh God, I'm so sorry!"

Instantly You grabbed me. Today, on April 30, 2003, You grabbed me! I actually felt You hugging me! Like a blanket. God! I can hear You! Why did I wait so long? This feeling is indescribable. Why did I wait so long? Nothing I've ever tried on this earth compares to a second of Your tangible presence. Nothing!

From my knees I jumped up. I felt loved. I felt life. For the first time, I felt really alive. I stepped out of a fog and into the light. I understood. I started laughing and crying and crying tears of joy, and it was messy but it was awesome, and I love You! And then I heard You. "Open your Bible," You said. "Wow, God, I heard that!" So I opened, and I read the first thing my eyes hit:

"I love the Lord for he heard my voice. He heard my cry for mercy. Because he turned his ears toward me, I will call on him as long as I live. . . . The chords of death entangled me, the anguish of the grave came upon me. I was overcome by trouble and sorrow. Then I called on the name of the Lord: Oh Lord, save me! . . . Be at rest once more, oh my soul, for the Lord has been good to you!" (Psalm 116)

O God, You wrote that for me! You heard me! You're speaking to me. Elated, I rejoiced, up on my feet and then balled on my bed, I rested. I finally rested, feeling Him holding me, His loving comfort. O, God how miraculous You are! I'm not worthy, yet, You heard my cry. All for You now, God. My life is all for You. One hundred and eighty degrees, and there's no turning back.

But then as I tried to see what lay ahead, I thought, "I'm scared."

You said, "Do not be anxious about the future. Today has enough worries of its own."

And I heard You!

Amidst the revelation, with everything streaming at once, inexpressibly excited, wanting to know You, wanting to know everything, I heard You say, "Day by day."

God, You heard me! You know me! Day by day, Jesus. Day by day. Thank You, God. I like it here. Out of the darkness and into the light. I am home, I am home. And I'm finally alive.

PART II

THE HEALING BEGINS

"Don't be afraid little warrior bride, victory's on the other side; you're not alone."

Jason Upton

Here's where I wish I could say I stopped making myself throw up. I wish I could say God miraculously healed me. It would have been easier. But He didn't. He's too smart (if I can even attribute that quality to God). He knew there was too much of me tied up into my dependence on bulimia, too many emotions stuffed inside that needed to be brought up and dealt with. If He took it away, I would have never learned to recognize my own emotions or the lies, the voice in my head masquerading as me. I may have stopped the eating disordered actions but not the thoughts.

I learned to start small—doing simple tasks that my counselor showed me. Through journaling and slowing things down, I began to understand my heart. If I didn't have an eating disorder to face, I would have never learned what my heart was truly hungry for.

CHAPTER 6

THE POWER OF TRUTH

OPENNESS is the first step in healing. As a new Christian, I tried to stop the bulimia. When I couldn't, I finally sucked up my pride and told Jim's fiancé, Eli, about it. They were the only Christians I knew I could trust. Bringing truth into the light is one of the hardest steps in the healing process. When you've lived in isolation, doing everything you can to keep your secret safe, the last thing you want to do is let anyone in on your secret. But it must be done. You will never be healed on your own. Trust me. Wrong relationships (competition, peer pressure, rejection, and wrong agreements) got you into this mess. Right relationships are going to get you out.

Eli was very patient and encouraging. She, too, had been bulimic when she was a model, but she was able to stop when she gave her life to God. I don't know why some people get healed right away and others don't. But it didn't stop me from believing. God knows what He's doing. She suggested I seek professional help.

In the meantime, I knew I couldn't wait around for a counselor to fix me. I was still struggling, trying to be a Christian, and falling flat on my face. I got involved in a church and sought mentorship. Here's where I had to go to another level of openness. When I finally told my mentor, Leah, about my struggle, it was awkward and embarrassing, but I knew if I wanted closeness I had to share that struggle.

The Power of the Word

Leah showed me the power of God's Word. It changed my life. You must attack the onslaught of lies with an onslaught of truth. Words are not just tools to communicate. They create. When God created the world, He determined that it would be words that caused everything to come into being. He spoke, and there was. Light was first. Nothing was hidden.

You were made in the image of God, born to carry His characteristics as a creator. Called to create in the light, you can't help but affect the supernatural realm when you speak, either negatively or positively. Sometimes you see the effects of your words immediately. In other situations, it takes time. What happens when a child hears the words, "You are stupid and worthless" over and over again? He begins to believe it. His appearance becomes downcast. He walks with his eyes to the ground and even acts differently. The negative words have created a different child. Sadly, his perceived reality is based on a lie.

On the other hand, if the same child hears the words, "You are a magnificent creation, capable of anything you put your hands to," his countenance gets brighter, his spirit gets lighter, and he begins writing down some of his ideas for new inventions, believing full well that he has what it takes.

The transformation did not happen simply because the words felt good. Words of life create life. Like an invisible paintbrush, words move in the unseen realm, painting what you end up seeing in the world around you.

Not only do words create, but God's Word, His truth, destroys darkness. There's a reason why His Word is called the Sword of the Spirit. It is a weapon capable of tearing the enemy to shreds if used properly. John 6:36 says, "The Spirit gives life. . . . The words I have spoken to you—they are full of the Spirit and life." His words breathe life into the places that are dead and dying.

So how do we use this sword? By having faith in what it says. How do we have faith? Romans 10:17 says, "Faith comes from *hearing* (continual verb) the message and the message is heard through the Word of Christ." So, we need to speak the truth out loud so we can *hear* it until we get a revelation of who we really are.

The enemy only has access to our lives when we don't know who we are. We are kings and queens, redeemed and seated with Christ in the heavenly places, but if we don't know that, the enemy can plant lies in our heads to define us. It's as if a homeless man was walking around sad and forlorn, but what he didn't know was that the whole time he had millions in the bank, hundreds of skills and talents to get any job he wanted, and a family who loved him, trying to get him to come home. The man somehow doesn't know the truth about his identity, so he wanders the streets.

You are royalty. A child of the Most High God. You are not alone. He's right next to you, calling you into His arms. His love and pursuit never changes. What changes is our ability to receive His love. We begin to receive when we get our receivers tuned to the right station. We've got to turn off the lies and tune in to what God is saying. This takes time, but speaking the truth out loud is a great place to start.

Lies Come from Several Sources

We hear lies from several sources. The most common is in our inner man. The lies play on loops like broken records, creating negative belief systems. Because I had said "I'm crazy, I'm fat, I'm stupid, and I'll never be free" for so long, I believed it. I created depression.

Not only do we hear lies in our inner man, but also voices speak to us all day long from billboards and magazines, TV ads and store windows. We must recognize the lies and have the words to dissolve their power. If the picture of the Victoria's Secret model is whispering, "You're fat and worthless. This is what men want, not your flabby body," I can agree or disagree.

We must change our belief systems in order to operate in the kingdom. The first step is recognizing the lie—after all, the messages are meant to enter our subconscious. The second step is knowing who you really are. We've got to have weapons to declare, "No, I'm not fat and worthless. I am a daughter of the Most High God! I am fearfully and wonderfully made, and right now you are terrified of me, enemy! So instead of listening to your intimidation, I'm gonna worship the one who loves me. Daddy God, praise You for making me so beautiful. For filling me up with so much joy and love. Praise You for holding me and delighting in me just as I am, right now, in this moment. I'm running to You, Dad! Thanks for creating me with such thought and care. I am so blessed to have the body that I have."

Confessing the Word

In order to help me fight the lies, Leah gave me a packet of Scriptures we called a confession sheet. (The book *Decrees* by Patricia King is an amazing tool as well.) I would read it out loud—faith comes by *hearing*—and confess its truth over my life. In the beginning, I didn't feel like doing it. I didn't even believe the words I was speaking. Most times I had to get up out of my pity party and force the words out. It was painful work at first. I didn't think it was helping, but the more I read it out loud, meditating on what I was saying, the more God's truth welled up in me. The words went into my being, creating life and transforming my thoughts until I actually believed what I was saying. I felt empowered. I felt alive.

The packet included Scriptures about "Who I am in Christ," "Victory," "Boldness," and so forth. I would pace the floor of my one-bedroom apartment declaring God's words, letting faith well up in me until soon I was practically yelling the verses. By faith, I even began swinging one hand in the air, visualizing the sword, beating the enemy and his filthy lies to a pulp. I would yell him into a corner, telling him I had defeated him "by the blood of the Lamb! By the words of my testimony! And not by loving my life unto death! I can do *all* things through Christ who strengthens me!"

I'm surprised the neighbors didn't complain. I mean really—I was ferocious. And I had to be. It was fight or be overcome, live or die.

The tongue holds the power of life and death, and if I keep telling myself I'm crazy or fat, I'll continue to kill my spirit. I have to speak truth. And it works! God's truth helps me be in tune with His reality, no matter how ugly my day is. I am a free woman and one who sets the captives free. I am not a victim. I was created for a purpose bigger than myself!

If our attack was physical, we wouldn't stand there and get beaten up. We would cry for help and fight back. So why be silent when our attack is spiritual? If you're always on the defensive, you'll get tired of getting beaten up. You've got to realize that with Christ, you are on the offense. You already have the victory.

Confessing the word isn't about the power of positive thinking. It's not 'name it claim it', and it's not about jumping through religious hoops. It's about surrendering our hearts to His truth. And when we surrender, we don't just agree with His Words in our minds, we burn with them.

Daily confess His Word. Let His truth overtake your consciousness. Thank Him for His promises. And I encourage you to come up with your own "confession sheet." The one I was given was general, so I created one that was specific to my struggle with eating disorders. The tongue has the power of life and death. Go ahead. Kick the devil's brains out! (See Appendix A and get going! Remember—out loud.)

CHAPTER 7

TIME FOR COUNSELING

THE next step in recovery was getting counseling. I never stopped meditating on the Word, but I had to go deeper. I couldn't stop the bulimic behavior and had no idea why. I needed another pair of eyes to help me see the lies and find my triggers. I found a good Christian counselor (we'll call her Jane) and began the tedious process of finding the roots of the problem. I had no idea where to start.

Trust me when I say that you cannot do this alone. While this book provides methods for healing, please do not try to proceed without a counselor or mentor. If you need help finding a counselor, please refer to the back of this book for a list of resources.

Journaling

As the sifting began, Jane recommended I keep a journal to document my "episodes." While I hated it at the time and thought it couldn't possibly help, I highly recommend it. Journaling helped me slow things down and describe what I was going through, what I was feeling. It helped me face the reality of what I was doing. This silenced denial.

Focusing on the episodes is a painful process. It may even bring up more disordered behaviors because you want to numb the pain you are suddenly feeling. That's OK. Press through. Force yourself to be as honest as possible. What were you thinking? What were you feeling? It may take a while until you are able to pinpoint thoughts and emotions, but that's just because you've never had to before.

It's amazing how thick denial can be. You may find yourself telling lies in your own journal. I did that most of the time, downplaying quantities or skipping parts. I couldn't even be honest with myself. But healing has to start somewhere.

I've included a few of my first journal entries in italics. I must warn you, it's not pretty. I've included them only so you know you are not alone. They are a picture of my battle. Your struggle may look different, but know that nothing is too shameful or "crazy" to be brought into the light.

Here it goes:

Green Journal Entry No. 1: May 2, 2004

This is my first journal entry on my road to recovery. I hope it's a short road. I don't want to do this journal. My counselor says it will help. I think it's stupid. But I need to do this. I owe it to myself. I'll try anything. I'm sick. I need to get better. I just want it all behind me.

Describe your bingeing habits:

My episodes of bingeing and purging vary. Sometimes I'd be writing a paper and eating carrots. I'd keep eating because the oral fixation helps me concentrate. Then all of a sudden I'd be full. The feeling of fullness automatically triggered the thought that I'm fat. So I decide to purge. But before I do, I might as well take this opportunity to eat what I normally deny myself. It's coming up anyway . . . so I'd eat more. Purge, and that'd be the end.

But the worst episodes can consume an entire day, lasting on into the next day. I might do it every day. Some nights I really lose it . . .

Usually I would get anxious, about God knows what (school work, my weight, boredom, loneliness, feelings of worthlessness??), and start to eat whatever I had at home (which is never good binge food because I only keep tasteless healthy stuff here). Then unsatisfied, I'd drive to Ralph's and grab whatever looked good and what I knew would come up easily. I'd steal candy from the barrels. Sometimes I'd open packages of dried pineapple, eat a few and put the package back on the shelf when I got sick of them. That way, I wouldn't have to pay for it.

I'd come home already eating on the way, desperate, anxious, stuffing whatever I bought into my mouth until I reached the breaking point. Then

I'd get in the shower with my big plastic cup and purge and purge and purge
until I was sure it was all out. Every type of food accounted for.

I would hurt. My eyes would water, my heart would race. Then I'd clean
any splashes, clean up the kitchen counters, get myself together and sit for a
little while, sometimes in front of the TV, ignoring what I'd just done. Not
wanting to deal with anything. Trying to ignore the voice that said I wanted
more food.

Then, unable to stand it, I would hit up 7-11. Come home and do the
same violent thing all over again. Then get up, walk to Cold Stone. Buy for
two. Do it again. I would do this until the stores around me all closed.

Usually I would end up purging in a pitcher in the shower. I felt so dirty.
The shower helped me feel clean. It hurt. I'd get dizzy, my head pounding
with pressure, eyes burning, literally drained, out of control, frantic, thinking
to myself, Why are you doing this? You're crazy!

It was these extreme times that would land me naked in a ball on my
bed, feeling hopeless, angry. Not wanting to say anything to God. Frustrated,
lonely, self-pitying, and empty. Not having enough energy to cry—to deal with
anything—I'd stare into space, with depression on my face. Wanting so badly to
be held. Wanting to be hugged. I'd close my eyes and long for my mom to come
and tell me it was OK, to stroke my forehead and let me sleep. I felt like a needy
little girl.

But something always prevented me from reaching out. Pride.

Journal Entry continued:

Other times I did it in restaurants. Or even other people's homes. This
was rare, but as long as I knew it was safe (like the bathroom was far away
or a single), I'd eat more than I needed.

Sometimes the binges were planned. I'd be waiting to get off work or
school, thinking about what I was gonna eat to drug myself. Then I'd go
to the store with my favorite binge foods in mind, frantic on the inside,
but calm on the outside, even getting on my cell phone, and pretending to
be talking to someone about what kind of ice cream or candy they wanted,
or pretending it was someone's birthday party so it didn't look as if I was
getting all that food for myself. Come to think of it, the phone technique is a
common one I use. It helps me hide. But I always feel so guilty.

Sometimes I'd try to stop by throwing the binge food away, but then I'd end up digging in the trash moments later. The trash!

I've had incidents of not being able to get stuff back up. Those times have been pure torture: knowing there still has to be at least six doughnuts still in there, desperately trying anything to get it back up, sticking the bent over end of my hairdryer cord down my throat as deep as it could go. It hurt really badly, but all I could think about was getting those doughnuts out.

Most of the time my head is swarming, my body feels tense and my teeth clench (my counselor taught me to notice these things). There's a Ping-Pong game inside my head: Do it, don't do it. Come on. It's no big deal. Man, but you almost made it five days in a row without doing it. But you know you'll feel so much better. No! Don't blow it! O, but who cares? Nobody will know. . . .

Through therapy, which I've been doing for almost eight months, my binges have gone from a couple of times every day to as low as once a week. I've made major breakthroughs, all revolving around relationships (mom, dad, brother, best friend, God). God has been pushing me to reach out to others.

Overall my episodes vary in duration, intensity, and frequency. It all depends on how out of control I get, what I choose to buy, how distant I feel from God, from people. Many times I feel I can't come to God. Don't want to. I feel as though I'm really not forgiven, or He's sick of hearing me whine and say the same "forgive me" prayer over and over again. Or maybe I just get sick of saying it. . . .

This entry was very hard to write. I left many details out. I even wrote in the past tense, as if I wasn't still in the middle of the mess. Speaking in past tense was also a part of the denial, but writing helped me take a more active role in my healing. I can't expect others to fix me.

Lighten Up

While processing all of this information, one important thing for me to remember was to lighten up. I was always so hard on myself. It was important that while recording all of these episodes in gruesome detail, I continued to remind myself to lighten up. Jude 1 says, "Relax, everything's going to be all right; rest, everything's coming together; open your heart, love is on the way" (The Message).

So instead of getting frustrated or mad at myself, I had to keep remembering that this was all a part of the healing process. I had to learn to give myself grace. I am not a project; I am a daughter, and I don't always have to analyze my problems.

Because writing about the battles helped me slow things down, I was able to pinpoint some specific emotions. Years of building protective walls had dulled my senses. I had to recover them:

August 29, 2004

After a binge/purge I feel:
Dull
Dead
Drained
Numb
Emotionless
Unmotivated
Slow
Lifeless
Paused
I stare at my face
I stare at my body
I feel
Stuck
Angry
I scowl, frown
I feel like I disappeared

BUT
I am NOT dead
I am alive in Christ
Sin has no dominion over me!
I will resist the devil, and he will flee!

The Cycle of Emotions

Journaling also helped me realize the cycle of emotions I went through when I resorted to bulimia. The cycle would usually begin with feelings of failure or worthlessness. These thoughts would play like tapes on a loop in my head until I felt utterly powerless. I felt as if I had no control over my life. Resorting to bulimic behavior was my way of feeling effective, as if I could fix the feelings and make everything OK. Then came the high, which I received from the release of purging. Finally, there was the hope that this would be the last time. For some reason, I always thought that this purge would be the final solution to everything. I couldn't think past this one purge. Finally, I returned to feelings of worthlessness and shame. Sometimes there was a period of peace and numbness after the purge, but this was fleeting. When the numbness subsided, I was still a lonely, isolated girl who knew deep down that the bulimia wasn't helping.

May 23, 2004

I really don't want to write. Everything inside me says no.

OK, fine . . . so I feel crazy. Like something's got hold of me. I can feel its fingers gripping and strangling me. I gave up. I'm mad. At God. At myself. At life. I'm pushing myself back down here . . . how do I pull out!? I feel cut off, separated from love. Drifting. My line drifts tattered. I can see it. The rock is shrinking as I fall deeper and deeper into the angry red waters. O God! I don't want to kill myself anymore! Bring me back! I wanna be close. Why is it so hard!? Why can't You just fix me!? I can't live like this. Don't want to live like this. With my head barely above water.

The angry red sea laps at my nostrils. Threatening. Taunting. It looks so blue and peaceful down there. I want it. To just let go and sink. It would be so much easier. It was easier before I started fighting back.

Come on, Jessica! Don't think that! It would be a horribly lonely death. You know that. Look closer. Now do you see? I can hear their shrieks, feel them swimming around me, biting away at my toes. I see the truth. It's not peaceful; it's worse down there.

No! I will not surrender! You can't have me! I am the daughter of the King! Lord, You are good, and You will rescue me!

Journaling and being honest is like getting the poison out. I had to tell God I was mad at Him for not healing me, mad at Him for making it so hard. Sure, He could read my mind, but as a friend of mine once said, "Eavesdropping does not constitute a relationship."

Once the poison was out, I could more freely grab onto His truth. I had to declare His goodness no matter what—as in many of David's Psalms.

> *A psalm of David.*
> *"How long, O LORD ? Will you forget me forever?*
> *How long will you hide your face from me?*
> *How long must I wrestle with my thoughts*
> *and every day have sorrow in my heart?*
> *How long will my enemy triumph over me?*
> *Look on me and answer, O LORD my God.*
> *Give light to my eyes, or I will sleep in death;*
> *my enemy will say, "I have overcome him,"*
> *and my foes will rejoice when I fall.*
> *But I trust in your unfailing love;*
> *my heart rejoices in your salvation.*
> *I will sing to the LORD,*
> *for he has been good to me." (Psalm 13)*

Even in times when David felt beaten down and distant from God, he always confessed his ultimate trust in the Lord.

August 30, 2004

> *OK, so I just had a 15-minute session my counselor. I had nothing to say, so she said I could go.*
> *I feel so stupid and childish. I feel as if I'm wasting my time. I should be healed by now. I feel embarrassed. Like she's wondering why I don't stop wasting her time and get my life together already. I feel as if I have more to share, but I don't know what. I feel tired. Come on already! Haven't I been sawing enough! Why are you still here!! You're like this burden that waits for*

me at the end of a slacked chain. I walk away from you, but you pull me back again. You trap me. Paralyze me and make me stare into space. My brainwaves slow in the aftermath of your violence. You laugh at me from the mirror as I stare.

Right now I feel slow. Apathetic. I don't want to think. This apathy tries to pawn responsibility off onto others. "Fix me," it says. "Tell me something that will make me feel good. Motivate me." That's why I had to leave my counselor's office. I had no energy to talk. It's too much effort to pull myself up when I feel this way. I just don't get it. I want help, but I don't want to be a burden.

Stop being so childish! Wake up and get yourself out of this!

At first I didn't want to leave the office. Inside I thought, No, let's talk. Help me. I know I can think of something to say. But there was nothing. Is anything significant? Do I do any of this for a reason anymore? Is my counselor frustrated with me? I feel bitter toward her. Why does she get to tell me the session is over? I'm the one that needs help! She's skinny. She doesn't have problems.

Anyway, I trust her, I guess. Lord, help me. You know what You're doing. Have Your way. Help me to get out of this cave inside my head. This emotionless, boring cave. It's restless in here.

Why can't someone just fill in the blanks for me!?

This is what you're feeling:_____

This is why:_____

This is how you fix it:_____

Choosing Life

Many times I wanted to give up. I didn't feel as if I had anything new to learn or anything to say to my counselor. But I had to keep pressing through, choosing life every day, knowing that deep down I would one day be free.

October 1, 2004

O Lord it cripples me! O Jesus take it away! O Lord hold me! Pull me out of this hole. I know You want me to get up. But O Lord, I don't think I can.

I'm so tired of fighting. It's been so long. Over a year of fighting this thing. Too long! I don't want to wrestle with it any longer. Sometimes I make it two weeks without it, but I'm tired. Jesus, why can't I just stop! Sometimes depression just takes over. I just want to stay in bed all day. Don't want to deal with all the responsibility. It's too much. O Jesus, will this ever end!

But you O Lord are strong in my weakness. You never leave or forsake me. You quiet me in Your Word and still me with Your love. O Lord in Your anger, don't turn Your face from me. Lord when does the grace You give run out?

I have to make a decision every day. Today I choose life.

Journaling and sharing with a counselor is scary. Do I really want to be healed? How will I live without this control? Can I be healed without gaining weight? All of these questions will try to keep you bound. But that's where trust comes in. Trust God to lead you to the right counselor, and then trust that your counselor always has your best interest in mind. There may be times when you get mad at your counselor for recommending something you're not comfortable with, like seeing a dietitian. There may be times where he or she feels like an enemy. That's because healing is uncomfortable. Let go of the stubbornness that wants to keep everything neat and controlled. Counselors can see things that we cannot. Let him or her guide you. Try things out even when you disagree.

CHAPTER 8

FINDING TRIGGERS

WRITING not only helped make the battle more real, but it also helped me uncover my weaknesses, the triggers that lead me to binge and purge. I thought there was no rhyme or reason behind my binges, but as I wrote, I began to recognize some of my emotions and therefore uncover my triggers. Sometimes it was boredom and loneliness that lead me to binge. Other times it was social anxiety, hiding behind mouthfuls of Chex Mix at a birthday party. Sometimes I binged because I was beating myself up in my head for saying something stupid or not doing something perfectly. I was extremely hard on myself.

The more I wrote, the more I was able to see patterns in my life that lead me to binge and purge.

August 3, 2004

No! I am not going back to my cave again! Tonight I struggled. It started with the doughnut. Why'd I eat that disgusting thing? Then snacking at Sarah's. Then I ate the dried pineapple at the store. I said no pineapple. This rule was broken, so I got mad. Definitely a trigger. I should have at least been happy that I didn't steal it like I usually do. It almost made me madder that I paid for that crap.

Man, then the drive to my parent's house in Newport always gets me anxious (another trigger). Why? I need to enjoy the drive. Slow down. Talk to God.

Jesus, forgive me. Lord, how do I change? Why do I do what I don't want to do? So I arrived in Newport and kind of avoided my parents' hugs at the front door. I don't want them to see through me. Mom bothers me when she gets all clingy. Lord, forgive me. Give me patience.

Then at the dinner table I ate my whole big salad because there was tension. Man, I was stuffed, and I hated it. How do I cope with my sensitivity to such tension so I don't feel bottled up all the time? I feel like a pressure cooker. Just frustrated but holding in my annoyance. I flee toward food. It's like I hide my anger behind bitter mouthfuls. If I just keep eating, I don't have to be a part of the conversation. Don't have to make eye contact.

That's a lie! Hiding in food makes me feel so much worse! I need to say I'm sorry to my mom for making the "you're so negative" comment. I get so prideful and stubborn and hide behind food.

God help me. I'm coming up against some serious challenges that I need to recognize: a whole week with the family—always hard, tempting food that they keep in the house, easy privacy in my room, also I'm gonna be in a bathing suit—always a trigger.

Be On Guard

As I discovered my triggers, I was able to be on guard. One of my triggers was going home to my parents' house. Home was a place of old habits, anxiety, and fear of exposure. There always seemed to be tension for me around my parents. I was quick to isolate myself.

In addition, I knew the freezer was always stocked with Häagen-Dazs ice cream. I'd stay up later than my parents, watching TV, which I realized almost always led to a binge and purge. The ice cream would begin calling to me from the freezer: "I'm so yummy, and you know you want me. You never get the chance to eat me, and you know I taste so good. And I'm free. Come on over and have at me!"

Because I recognized this weakness, whenever I went home, I prepared myself ahead of time. First, I acknowledged the battle that was bound to ensue. I also declared that I could win it because God had already given me the victory. I just had to grab hold of it.

Second, I devised a plan of action to keep myself far from temptation. Because I knew my weakness with staying up late, I determined to go to bed or at least go upstairs to my room when my parents went to bed. That way I wouldn't be alone so close to the kitchen. The Bible encourages us to flee from temptation. This makes the battle much easier.

I learned that it was incredibly easy to talk myself out of fleeing. I always felt as if I deserved those few cookies I started munching on as soon as my parents went upstairs. "It's normal to have dessert after dinner," I rationalized. But then why was I too ashamed to eat them while my parents were with me? There was more to those cookies than I let myself believe. That's why I had to have a plan ahead of time.

War strategists do the same thing. They devise a plan of attack and choose to follow through. When the time came to fight, if soldiers suddenly wanted to turn around or thought that maybe they could get the enemy to play a game of soccer, they would get blindsided. Why? Their minds weren't in the fight. They let their emotions in the moment determine their actions.

Most times I didn't want to fight in the moment. In the moment, I didn't think watching TV after everyone went to bed was going to be a problem or even that eating one cookie would be a problem. I was great at lying to myself: *It's fine. Just relax. Just one more cookie.*

It's never a good idea to trust a voice that has led you into death time and time again. So I learned to go to extreme measures and force myself to get in bed with a book instead. TV robbed me of joy anyway. Too many lying voices and images.

The next time you feel yourself wanting to give into the eating disorder, slow things down. Write about it. Instead of asking why ("Why God? What's wrong with me? Why does this happen to me?"), ask, "How did I get here?" Ask yourself what kinds of feelings you are going through. What situation just happened? Is there an impending situation causing anxiety? Is it a certain person? Are you comparing yourself? Staring at other women? Staring in the mirror? Where have your thoughts been? You must take your thoughts captive.

Begin the journey of recognizing your triggers. Trust me; they're there. And it's worth every ounce of energy to find them. Once you start recognizing them, plan ahead. Get your mind on the offense. Determine your steps of action, and learn to follow through. With His help, all things are possible.

CHAPTER 9

REASONS TO FIGHT

WHEN I began to go for counseling, I knew that the road would not be fun or easy. Nobody else was going to fix me, or find my triggers, or unfold my own emotions and thoughts for me. I had to fight. In order to maintain the motivation to fight, I had to understand why I wanted to be healed. Even this was difficult at first. I knew I didn't like living with my head in the toilet, but I didn't really know how my life would be different without bulimia. What would I do if I wasn't obsessing at the gym, grocery shopping, tanning, etc. . . . ? So I sat down and made a list. I kept it so I could be reminded of why I wanted to say no to the enemy. Here are my reasons:

Reasons Why I Want To Be Healed

- So I can grow in intimacy with God
- So I can know my true identity and worth
- So my children will have a healthy mother
- So they won't have to deal with the same issues I do
- So I can share myself freely with my friends and be there for them when they need me
- So I can be present
- So I stop wasting money
- So I can be truly alive and live a long life
- So others can see somebody walking in victory
- So when I get married my husband will have a wife with whom he can truly connect
- So I will be able to hear You clearly, God
- So I will live the amazing life God has for me

- So I will have a testimony of His strength
- So I can build intimate relationships with friends
- So I can live in honesty
- So I can have pure joy
- So I can take my eyes off of myself
- So I don't have to live in fear of being caught
- So I don't have to cover my tracks
- So I don't have to have food always on my mind
- So I can be more productive with the time God has given me and do the things I really want to do
- So I can be focused on serving and seeing and loving others
- So I will be more perceptive to where God is leading me
- So people can see Me in you, Jessica

Because I teach out of who I am—
and being bulimic kills who I truly am

Because Every Time I Do It

- I grieve Jesus
- I don't feel good
- I feel disconnected from people
- I can't look people in the eye
- I am killing my body
- I am destroying the interior of my stomach and intestines
- I am spiritually dying
- I am choosing a path that leads to death, spiritually and physically
- I can't hear God as well
- I hide myself from God and the world
- I feel depressed
- I feel dishonest
- I forget about others
- I am being selfish and prideful
- I let myself be deceived
- I waste time
- I waste money

- I ruin friendships
- The devil laughs

It's good to know the weapons in your arsenal. A list like this will help when all you want to do is give up. It will help you place a heavy price tag on the decision to give in. Sometimes all we need is a good jolt of reality.

Something God told me that really increased my desire to fight is this: *Your battle is not just about you. It's about a generation after you. As you fight and resist the enemy, you are gaining ground for an entire generation!* "The body is a unit, though it is made up of many parts; and though all its parts are many, they form one body. So it is with Christ" (1 Corinthians 12:12).

What we do affects the body because we are all together in the same war. Each of your victories is someone else's victory. You're not alone. Make a list of reasons to fight. It will help you persevere until the end.

CHAPTER 10

MYTHS

EATING disorders are composed of a false framework of rules. I had a whole slew of these myths keeping me bound. They involved things like what and when I could and couldn't eat, or for how long I had to work out on any given day. If I broke just one of these rules, or my schedule was interfered with, I was thrown into a tailspin.

Instead of listening to my body's cues, the rules told me what to do. It was too scary to live without them—there were too many food decisions, diet tricks, and workout formulas to know what was good and what was bad. So I created my own rules. I occasionally added rules or changed them if I picked up on a diet tip from an ad or overheard a conversation at the gym about a better way to burn fat. But for the most part, I clung to what I'd been doing.

In addition to rules, I had also developed assumptions regarding people's perspective of me. Together, these paradigms distorted my view of reality. Instead of the truth, I was living a life based on myths. In order to be free, I had to discover these myths and change them. One by one, I began tearing down this false framework of thoughts that was keeping me in prison, keeping me from being as free as a three-year-old.

For example, one of my myths was, "If I feel full, it means I am fat." Every time I felt full, even if it was just full of diet soda, my spirit and emotions would scream, "I'm fat, I'm fat, I'm so gross!" I had to let my mind consider, "Well, all I really had was a Diet Coke, which has no calories. And besides, it's physically impossible to gain five pounds of body fat in an hour." I then had to help my emotions calm down and understand this. I spoke God's truth over my life with my rational mind. I had to let it wash over me until my spirit grabbed hold of its truth.

I realized that I felt whatever I was meditating on. If I was meditating on the thought that "I'm fat," I felt very uncomfortable in my own skin. If I was meditating on "I'm free and beautiful, and I wonder what's going on in other people's lives," then I felt free. I was free to engage with others because I felt confident.

One of my steps to healing involved writing out a list of "myths I want to change." Of course, I didn't think they were myths at first, but they were, and they were keeping me bound. Here's the list I made:

1. If I feel full, I am fat, even if I'm really just full from a diet peach iced tea Snapple.
2. If I miss my quiet time in the morning with God, my whole day will be spent out of God's presence because He's disappointed with me.
3. No sandwiches because bread has too many unnecessary calories.
4. If I'm full, other people notice my huge bulging stomach.
5. Other people look at me and are disgusted that I let myself get so out of shape. I was prettier before when I was anorexic.
6. I have to eat X amount of calories every X hours because if I don't my metabolism will get messed up and I'll get fat.
7. I therefore have to eat at home and/or bring food with me, planning every meal and snack to stay in control.
8. If I eat one bad thing (e.g., a piece of candy) my whole day is ruined, so I might as well eat unhealthily and purge later.
9. If I eat one bad thing I'm a failure, and if it stays in my body, I'll get fat.
10. Bad = carbs, sugar, fat, or too many calories.
11. If I skip a workout, I'll gain weight (because I feel sloppy and fat and lazy).
12. People judge my character by how much weight I gain or lose. (If I'm fat, it means I have no self-control and am lazy.)
13. People notice when I eat unhealthy things and think, *She shouldn't be eating that. She needs to lose weight.* That's why I usually do it in secret, so I won't be judged.
14. I can't eat past X o'clock at night because if I do, I'll get fat
15. When people see me eating healthy, they think, *Why is she even trying? It's obviously not doing her any good.*
16. If I go out to eat, I can only order salads with no dressing.
17. People notice all of the flaws in my body. It grosses them out.

It's obvious to me now that all of these rules and assumptions are myths, feigned and imaginary. They were created out of a fear of not being accepted. Over the years, beginning with early childhood, the lies about my identity built up. Each feeling of being misunderstood, awkward, unseen, or not as pretty as so-and-so added to my fear of rejection. I had to create rules to be safe and accepted. But instead of making me feel safe, the rules only added to my false assumptions and fear of rejection. Thus my neurotic ideology.

What I thought were simply ways to stay thin were actually chains keeping me isolated, keeping me from expressing my true self. I feared breaking a rule, and I feared what people thought of me.

Judging Others

Ironically, many of these fears came about because of the way I judged others. I judged what others ate and didn't eat and how much weight they gained or lost. I wrongly judged heavy people for eating junk food. Romans 2:1 says, "It takes one to know one. Judgmental criticism of others is a well-known way of escaping detection in your own crimes and misdemeanors" (The Message). O, how true that is.

Because I focused on judging other people's eating habits and appearance, I felt the weight of their "judgment" on me. I say "judgment" because the truth was, they weren't judging me. Matthew 7:1-2 warns, "Do not judge, or you too will be judged. For in the same way you judge others, you will be judged." Because I noticed what others ate and didn't eat, I felt as if they noticed and judged what I ate as well. The less I judge others, the less I feel that people are judging me. Amazing how that works.

Discover Your Myths

Before this exercise, I was unaware that I had so many rules and assumptions that were running my life and keeping me from being me. But since I learned the truth, I've been able to dissolve these myths one by one. I encourage you to discover your myths. Confronting the myths will help melt your protective barriers so you can finally breathe. Some may be harder to find because they have been a part of your "reality" for so long. They seem healthy. But once you start writing, you will be surprised at how much your mind is working against you.

CHAPTER 11

THE SCALE AND THE MIRROR

BEFORE we go any further, I need to point out two of the biggest liars in your life: the scale and the mirror. Knowing that these two objects lie will make the battle much easier. You must eliminate these sources of lies.

The Scale

Remember how I mentioned that when I became anorexic, the scale and the mirror became my new best friends? Well, on my road to recovery, the scale was the first thing to go.

Tossing out the scale may not be easy, but it must be done. If you're not strong enough, take it into your counselor's office with you, or tell a friend and have a scale-bashing party. It's lying to you anyway.

You are not a number. A number cannot define you. By holding onto the scale, you are giving a lifeless object power. A number should not hold the power to make you feel happy or depressed. It should not be able to tell you if you're a success or a failure, beautiful or ugly. Only God can define you, and He calls you lovely. And despite what you might think, He's not just saying that to flatter you or because He thinks everyone's beautiful even when they're not. What He says is reality. You are beautiful. Behold this truth. Let it sink in. What you behold is what you become.

The Mirror

Despite what God says about me, I still have trouble receiving His truth when I behold myself through the wrong filters. My eyes have been tainted by images of perfect bodies passing before me on TV, in ads, and all around me here in San Diego. My definition of beauty has been skewed. Because of this, beholding myself in the mirror has posed major problems. All I could see was what was wrong with me and what needed to be fixed. I had to learn to stop wasting hours in front of that darn mirror.

The mirror has been a little more difficult to get away from than the scale. After all, I didn't want to walk out of the house in the morning with something on my face. I had to look. But I did go through a season where I forced myself to take only quick glances at the mirror before I left the house. I had to ditch the little handheld mirror that helped me check out my butt. I always felt depressed after looking at that one, no matter how skinny I was.

Another step in the freedom was avoiding the full-length mirror as I was getting dressed and undressed. This helped me not be terrified by my changing body at the beginning of recovery. The mirror lied anyway.

Once I was free from an unhealthy addiction to staring in the mirror, trying on outfit after outfit, poking and prodding, dissecting every inch of my naked body from every angle, I had to reach a place where the mirror was safe, where it no longer controlled my emotions. I had to learn to look in the mirror, and, instead of picking on myself, choose to compliment myself despite my feelings: "Jessica, you look beautiful. Thank You, Jesus, for making me the way I am. Thank You for these legs and arms. Thank You for this stomach, this butt, and this skin. Thank You. It is lovely because You fashioned it." Later I began to hear God Himself complimenting me. This always made me shine brighter and even caused me to laugh out loud.

I had to go through the same process when I saw my own reflection in store windows. First, I had to avoid looking completely. Otherwise, glancing at myself would often shatter any confidence I had when I left that morning. "Man, I look like that?" Then I went from avoiding reflections to glancing at reflections and saying, "You look beautiful." Now I rarely think about reflections. It's a great freedom. I love it when I find I'm too focused on other people to worry about what I look like. Sometimes it still takes a conscious effort to not look. If I do look, I try to simply say, "Thank You, Jesus." I'm much freer knowing the mirror can't control my emotions.

Freedom from the scale and mirror may take time, but take baby steps if you have to. And always remember, you are not a number. And you are not what you see in the mirror. You are His precious child, the object of His affection, and that alone gives you all the worth you will ever need. The next time you catch yourself spending too long in the mirror, choose to walk away. Declare that the King is enthralled with your beauty.

Freedom from the scale and mirror is a key step in healing. Once you can walk away, you will realize more and more that your identity does not lie in a number or a reflection. Your identity is the spirit inside, which longs to be free to shine.

CHAPTER 12

GUARD YOUR GATES

"THE eye is the lamp of the body. If your eyes are healthy, your whole body will be full of light. But if your eyes are unhealthy, your whole body will be full of darkness" (Matthew 6:22-23). Our eyes and ears are the most receptive gateways into our physical and spiritual bodies. The biggest sources of the darkness that comes streaming into these gates are the TV, magazines, and music.

Growing up I frequently bought *Teen* and *Seventeen* magazines. I didn't see anything wrong with it. I just knew it was the cool thing to do. I liked looking at all the cute clothes and accessories and reading all the funny gossip columns and "most embarrassing moment" stories. But what was happening to me over the years? What was being reinforced in my malleable little spirit as I turned page after page of perfectly put-together girls and stories about their latest crush? That this was how I was supposed to look. If I didn't, there was something wrong with me.

As I grew older, the magazines 'matured' into *Cosmopolitan* and *People*. It was just something to mindlessly peruse on a lazy Saturday at the beach. And there were the TV shows that everyone was obsessed with. We built entire cultures around our favorite shows with weekly gatherings, anything for an excuse to get together and escape into another world. And would you guess what types of people were featured on all of these shows? Ordinary looking people? Heavens no. Television programmers cannot afford to put an ordinary face on the screen. Every show is loaded with gorgeous men and women, but because it's so normal to find perfect faces on TV, it's easy to forget about all the procedures these people have gone through to look that way.

The magazines and TV shows were doing nothing to help my self-esteem. I began idolizing the models' and actors' bodies and outfits, comparing myself to them, picking up on ways in which men and women interacted with one another, which usually consisted of the woman wearing sexy outfits and being playfully flirtatious at all the right times. It consisted of drama that should never be a part of everyday life. And even though my life was never as dramatic, I began seeing patterns for living that went against the way were we were created to live.

But can TV shows really be that powerful? In 1995, a woman by the name of Ann Becker performed a study of the effects of TV on the Fijian culture. Shortly after TV was introduced in Fiji, 3 percent of the girls had started vomiting to "control weight." Their favorite show was *Baywatch*. In 1998, Becker returned and found that the number had increased to 15 percent! No matter what we think, the facts speak for themselves.

And music is the same way, subtly pumping cultural norms into our ears. The music at the gym always seemed to have something to do with someone's tight, sexy butt. Apparently, those are the only ones that are acceptable.

I used to think that staying away from certain TV shows or magazines was just a religious act and that the adults who talked about the bad influences of such media didn't know anything about being cool. Now I know the reasons to stay away. They only rob me of my self-esteem. At first it took a conscious effort to stay away from the magazines, especially at the checkout stand in the grocery store. There was always some article about weight loss grabbing my attention. But I knew I had to guard what I was putting into my ears and eyes.

Now I don't even think about looking at those magazines or watching those shows or listening to that music because I live in a different world. There's not a bone in my body that desires those things. But it started with an awareness of what those sources were doing to my spirit.

What shows, magazines, or music do you allow into your gates that are preventing you from progressing in your freedom? Whatever you let into your gates will eventually be seen on the outside. For if your eyes are healthy, your whole body will be full of light. But if your eyes are unhealthy, your whole body will be full of darkness. Are your eyes looking at light or darkness? Choose to fill yourself with light. The more you do, the more your whole body will shine with His glory.

CHAPTER 13

DANCE BREAKS AND ALTERNATIVE ACTIVITIES

A S I was going through all of these big changes, it seemed as if I was getting worse instead of getting better. There were so many new things to focus on. My emotions were no longer numb. I had to learn to take dance breaks when I found myself getting too overwhelmed, analytical, or critical. I even resorted back to a childhood pastime of mine: making faces at myself in the mirror. Being able to laugh at myself is so freeing. I would jump up from the computer, ice skate across the floor in my socks, and let out an exuberant yelp as I leapt across the room. Haha! I thought it was the funniest thing ever! Finally, I was enjoying myself.

Remember to lighten up. You're doing great. Dance around the room and be silly and goofy. Enjoy yourself! God loves playing with you, and He really enjoys your sense of humor. Delight in yourself. Delight yourself in Him. He'll give you that smile your heart needs.

Be proud of yourself, too. No one's a bigger critic of yourself than you are. Anytime you feel overwhelmed, take a deep breath, get off your bum, and dance around the room—I mean really dance. Flail your arms and make yourself look ridiculous. Laugh! Make faces in the mirror if you want. Fly a kite. Go roller skating. Be a kid again.

A three-year-old doesn't worry about what other people think. And they don't try to do everything perfectly. They just do things, like run out onto the dance floor at weddings, squealing with delight and shaking their booties.

Know that you are delighted in. Be as free as a three-year-old!

Alternate Activities

In addition to learning how to delight in myself, my counselor helped me create a list of alternate activities to do every time I felt like bingeing. It helped to be prepared ahead of time. That way I already knew I had other options when bingeing and/or purging felt like the only choice, or when I didn't know what else to do with my time. As I began to engage in other activities, I was able to take the time to discover what I was really hungry for. I slowly learned that most often what I really desired was to talk to a friend or to God, or to say something that needed to be said, or even to take some time to breathe and find relaxation in a hot bath.

I came to realize that my eating disorder had less to do with food and more to do with my emotions. For so long, I had stuffed my emotions and desires deep inside. The bingeing and purging was a symbolic act of my desire to get all of my stuffed emotions out of me. Because I had no idea how to do that, bingeing and purging had taken the place of being open.

I made a list of alternate activities to do when my emotions built up and all I thought I wanted was food. Leaving the house and going on walks was one of my favorite activities. I learned that most times I just needed room for my spirit to breathe, to expand, to smile at the children playing in the park and at the sun setting over the ocean. I found room for my soul to take delight in the Lord, in myself, and in everyone around me.

Other times I would fill up the tub, light some candles, and treat myself to a nice, relaxing soak. I found I rarely took time for myself, which was why I ended up with so much anxiety. I felt that I always had to be productive. I didn't deserve luxuries.

Here's a list I made of alternate activities:

- Go on a walk or jog
- Confess the Word over my life
- Draw or paint
- Drive to a place with an amazing view and watch the ocean
- Go roller blading around the bay
- Grab a good book and go to a coffee shop
- Go on a bike ride

- Call a friend and see if they want to join me for any of the above activities
- Get out of the house and call a friend just to say hi or to talk about my feelings
- Get out of the house and call my mom
- Sit on a park bench and write poetry
- Take a hot bath
- Learn about something I've always wanted to know about

Getting out of the house was a huge deal for me. Staying indoors usually kept me hunting in the pantry or fridge, snacking on unsatisfying snacks, which then led me to the grocery store. I made sure to leave my money at home when I went on the walks. That way I couldn't fool myself into stopping at 7-11.

I also found that I could stop the process at any moment, in the middle of a binge, or even on my drive to the grocery store. Of course, it was always easier to stop the process before it started, but I actually learned to talk myself out of a binge mid-drive to the grocery store. Simply by using the tools mentioned, I've also stopped bingeing mid-binge. And I didn't throw up! Impossible? Not with the right truths under your belt.

If I was in a place where I couldn't just leave or take a bath, my counselor suggested I try running my hands under hot water or drinking hot tea. Something about those soothing sensations does wonders to calm nerves and satisfy the desire to be comforted.

So, make a list of alternate activities. You'll start to discover the things for which your heart truly longs.

CHAPTER 14

FOR FRIENDS AND FAMILY

I N Chapter 3, "Denial," I discussed the fact that many people don't know what to do when it comes to helping their loved one break free from eating disorders. It's hard for me to know what to do, and I've been there.

The one thing I can say is to *have compassion.* Your loved one is deeply hurting, whether they know it or not. Instead of thinking how gross they are, how frustrated you are, or trying to get them to eat, mention how much you love them and how concerned you are for them. How you've notice they've become secretive or withdrawn. Try to stick to emotional things instead of weight and food things.

You won't be received well. Know that giving up an eating disorder is extremely frightening for someone who has little or no experience being close to people or sharing feelings and emotions. It means risking rejection and facing painful realities. You'll probably be lied to. Don't take it personally. And never give up.

Don't Fall into Denial

First and foremost, loved ones need to admit that this is a serious problem and that it takes a great deal of uncomfortable work to heal. If you are a parent and people are calling you concerned about your child, listen to them. Don't fall into denial. I remember one girl who was showing all the signs of anorexia. She was extremely thin and was growing fur-like hair on her arms and back. Concerned, I called her mother. She said, "My daughter's fine. I know people are worried. She just has trouble keeping on weight." This may have been true, but I couldn't help but think this mother was deeply deceived. Her daughter had probably pulled all the stunts to keep her secret safe. Sometimes parents just don't want to believe that there could be something wrong with their child.

Because people with eating disorders become masters at hiding and lying to protect themselves, it's easy to be deceived. My parents didn't know about my secret until the mother of one of my friends called my mom and said, "Your daughter is not eating." My poor mom felt like a horrible mother. Why didn't she know this about me? Because I had become a master at hiding and pretending to eat.

Eating Disorders Are Misunderstood

Eating disorders are also extremely misunderstood. Because of this, they're usually either unnoticed or ridiculed. What you need to know is that it's not just about weight. It's about emotional bondage. My eating disorder (anorexia, at first) went unnoticed for eight months. My parents knew I was losing weight but thought it was because I was running and eating healthier. I didn't look anorexic. This is a common mistake. Most people in bondage to food do not look like skeletons. In fact, when my eating disorder was at it's worst as far as behavior was concerned, I looked the most "normal."

Also, people with eating disorders are usually very happy-looking, outgoing, and productive people. I hid my emotions well. Everything always looked fine on the outside. I was very social but knew I could withdraw at any minute to my safe repetitive routines. I may have appeared happy, present, and engaged in conversation, but usually my mind was light years away, thinking about food and my next or last binge.

In addition, you need to know that eating disorders are nothing to scoff at. If you suspect someone has an eating disorder, don't take it casually. It's common today to hear a group of girls gawking at a skinny girl passing by and say, "Ugh, she's totally anorexic." It hurts me to think that eating disorders are so misunderstood that others have no compassion. Many people believe eating disorders are about vanity, and they end up talking about that person behind their backs. Please know there is an unseen tangle of pain and destruction in the heart of someone with an eating disorder. It is not something to treat casually. Speak up. You could be the only one brave enough to address it.

Ignorance often allows the disorder to progress. Recently I mentioned to an acquaintance that I was writing a book. When he asked what it was about, I responded that it was about my recovery from eating disorders. "Oh, so it's like a health food book," he replied. At first I was offended. How could he be so ignorant? Then I realized that most people have no idea the depth to which the disorder reaches. It's not about not knowing how to eat. It's about rejection and self-hatred.

To help your loved one, get a better understanding of what eating disorders are all about. Educate yourself like you are doing now. Seek professional help to know how to deal with your loved one. Don't just stand by and hope they grow out of it. That won't happen.

It's important to note that men can struggle with eating disorders as much as women. Today, more and more men are revealing their struggle. While this book was written from a woman's point of view and may not be completely applicable to men, there are many great books written by men who have struggled. So don't discount the problem just because your loved one is male.

It's Not Your Job

Also, know that it is not your job to fix her (or him). If you are suspicious about a friend, tell them you love them, you are concerned for them, and you are there for them no matter what. Tell them you are there to listen. If you're a parent, you may not be the one your child wants to open up to. You may be part of the reason they are struggling, and so there may be too many walls up for them to want to be open with you. Don't get mad if they shove you away. Instead tell them how much you love them and that you'd be glad to help pay for a counselor they can talk to. They might not agree right away, but if they are under eighteen, you might have to exercise your rights. Do so with gentleness and compassion, but at the same time, do not allow yourself to be manipulated.

Also, do not be controlling of their life. The more you try to control, the more they'll want to fight against it, especially when it comes to food. It's not your job to set boundaries or follow them around to monitor her behavior. They will feel as if you have betrayed their trust. They needs to know that you are on their side, not sneaking behind their back. Don't constantly check up on them unless they ask that from you. Understand that they need to learn to make their own decisions and that recovery is their responsibility.

Above all, people who struggle with eating disorders need to know that they are loved. They don't need someone telling them what to do or how to eat. Just because you've educated yourself, that does not make you an expert on that individual. The worst thing is when someone tries to tell you what's wrong with you or claims to know how you're feeling. Don't try to guess what they want. Instead, encourage them to express their needs. Be a good listener. If you have questions, ask. But don't bring it up at the dinner table. It's extremely uncomfortable to talk about an eating disorder when around food.

Listen

Being an active listener is key in helping someone heal. Many of the feelings associated with eating disorders are those of being misunderstood and unseen. Your loved one is starving to be heard and known. On average, people tend to listen for about sixty seconds before interrupting and interjecting their own advice or opinions, instead of really trying to hear what is being said. Practice active listening.

Also, for the person with the eating disorder, there is a tremendous need to feel validated. Sharing is scary. I often felt as if I made no sense when I was sharing thoughts and feelings with my counselor and friend. My thoughts were always disjointed and convoluted. I felt like a freak. Because my counselor listened and then validated me by saying, "It makes sense to me that you might feel that way," I didn't feel like such a freak.

When I started dating a guy named Jesse—who is now my husband—I had been out of counseling for two years and had gone almost a full year without purging. Dating and our engagement brought on a whole slew of emotions that I was not ready to deal with. I had to tell him about my past, and the thoughts about food and my body that still tried to drag me down. It meant so much to me that he just listened. He asked how he could help. Because of this, I was able to tell him exactly what kind of support I needed. I didn't need a babysitter. I didn't want to feel as if he was always watching what I did or didn't eat. I knew he would only intervene or check in on me in ways I had asked him to.

There were times when I actually gave into bingeing and purging while we were dating. I felt so ashamed, as if I had failed, and I was embarrassed to tell him, but I knew by then that secrets were not what I wanted in any relationship. I called him, crying, telling him everything I'd done. I felt ashamed, dirty, and unworthy of love. He just listened and comforted me. He told me how proud he was of me for calling him and how he was confident that I could fight this. That was the best thing he could have told me.

Sometimes, all I want is someone there, not saying a word, just holding me. That way I feel safe and free to share when I'm ready. Jesse knew to just wait and hold me as I cried, allowing me to continue to share as needed. He'd encourage me to share by asking, "Do you want to talk about it?" or "Is there more you'd like to share?" Not only did that give me room to be open, but it also let me know that he was there to listen to my heart. He wanted to know me and was in it for the long haul.

It's always good before moving on to another subject to ask, "Is there anything else you'd like to share?" Then wait for a minute or so. Encourage your friend to also wait before answering. Most times there is much more they wants to share. Allowing for space is one of the best things you can do.

Compassion, Compassion, Compassion

I come back to this again and again because it is so important: Have compassion.

I always felt so repulsive and unlovable after giving in to the disorder. The last thing I needed was somebody asking me, "How did this happen?" or saying, "I thought you were through with this." I just needed to be held. To know I was still accepted, and loved and that I had someone on my team in whom I could confide and who would fight the lies with me. I needed to know I was free to share without feeling threatened.

Someone with an eating disorder does not need to be lectured or told they are sick. They need to be loved, to know that it's safe to be vulnerable. They need to be accepted, enjoyed, and smiled at. Don't treat them like a problem. Try to look into their heart. Offer to spend more time with them. Offer to go to a museum together or go for a walk. Plan activities that do not involve food. They need to know that they are worth your time and attention.

Focus on the Positive

Also, focus on the positive things about them. People with eating disorders are already hard enough on themselves. They doesn't need you telling them what they need to fix or how they're messed up. Try to stay away from physical characteristics as you compliment them. They already feels as if their worth is based on appearance. Call to the surface those amazing characteristics that may be buried deep inside. It's OK to tell them they're beautiful—I know I need to hear this all the time—but make sure they know it's not because of their clothes or the shape of their body.

If you are married, tell your spouse often how good looking they are. It's even OK to tell them you think their body is beautiful. They needs that reassurance. But make sure they know that you love *them* and that is why their body will always be beautiful to you, no matter what size it is. My husband Jesse is amazing at reassuring me of this. I always feel beautiful and free to share my body with him, no matter what shape it's in. He's made it clear to me that nothing, absolutely nothing, could make him change his mind. I know he's in love with *me,* and that includes my body in all shapes and sizes. I need to know that it's not a perfect body he's in love with.

Every once in a while I have a fear that Jesse might get bored of me or simply become unimpressed with my looks. This is because there are still a few roots of rejection trying to plant their way back into my head. When I bring this fear into the light, he is quick to squelch it with a barrage of reasons why he loves me, none of which have to do with the size of my body. He knows I'm not just fishing for compliments. I am dealing with a real fear that needs to be fought.

Become an expert at pointing out the positive. It's your loved one's job to learn to accept your words. Don't give up if your compliments are rejected. Know that your words are like a battering ram, breaking through their negative view of themself.

Be Patient

Know that healing takes time. It may take years. Many times there is an undefined end to the healing process. For instance, although I have not purged or gone on a massive binge in over a year, I do still struggle with the lies about my body from time to time. I find myself getting in slumps where I resort to food as a comfort, and it seems as though I am not *fully* recovered.

Be patient with your loved one. It's easy to get frustrated and say, "Stop doing that, already!" Healing seems so easy from an outsider's point of view, but you need to understand that there are deep tangles that need to be undone. It's no fun to feel as if people are disappointed in you for not healing faster. I remember I thought this about my counselor. I thought she must be frustrated that I had to deal with the same thing over and over again. But she wasn't. She was patient. Your loved one needs you to be patient.

Being patient will also help you be a better listener. I remember how frustrating it was to try and verbalize my thoughts and feelings. It helped to have a patient and understanding listener.

The journey to being open and sharing is a tough one, so be patient. Don't focus on the setbacks. Focus on the progress. And always be there to love and to listen.

Take Care of Yourself

Lastly, take care of yourself. If you're worn out and stretched thin, you won't be much help to your loved one. Being around an anxious, frustrated person will only egg the disordered behavior on. Relax, breathe, pray. Soak in a hot tub. Cast all your cares upon the Lord. Know the He can do far more than you ever could by worrying. Rest in the knowledge that He has your loved one in His loving arms. I am living testimony of this.

One day this will be all behind you.

PART III

THE ROOTS I FOUND

While learning to deal with my eating disorder on a daily level, I also had to go deeper—to go after the roots.

Going after the roots of my disorder was a crazy journey filled with many moments of wanting to run out the door. It was frustrating. Many times I felt as if I was getting worse instead of better. I hated not knowing what was going on inside me, answering every question with, "I don't know." But my counselor helped me process things. Together with God, we went after the places where the enemy took root. And God revealed them to me as I dug.

The pieces have to be brought to the surface, cleaned off, and reassembled—like after a plane crashes into the ocean. Divers are sent down to recover the pieces so the plane can be reassembled and studied to determine the cause of the crash—to get to the root of the problem. If the root problem isn't found, it's only a matter of time before another plane goes down.

I want to take you back there, back to the places where the roots of rejection began. There were people I needed to forgive and voices I needed to silence. Hopefully, this will help you go back and find memories of times in your life when you've been hurt and believed a lie. Disavowing the lies and embracing the truth are the biggest parts of the healing.

CHAPTER 15

LOOKING FOR APPROVAL AND FAMILY HISTORY

LOOKING for approval was how this whole thing began. I simply wanted to know that I was special, beautiful, funny, enjoyed, and seen. I wanted to be understood. I looked for approval in academics, I looked for approval in my social life, and I also looked for approval from guys and the girls I was competing against. But why did I look for approval in these ways? I had to look back at my family history to gain a better understanding.

Family History

The first people we look for approval from is our parents. I grew up with loving parents who wanted nothing but the best for me. Mom stayed home with me when I was little. She was so in love with me she says she could barely put me down. Dad loved, me too, but he was always working. The son of a workaholic, my dad was always at the office. My grandfather, William James Edwards Jr., had started a movie theater company in 1930 when he was twenty-three. Starting a business during the Great Depression was not easy. My grandparents ran the whole operation themselves, manning the ticket booth, screening the movies, and cleaning up the theater after shows. When the company was sold, it owned ninety theaters with more than 600 screens. Needless to say, my grandparents learned the benefits of hard work.

This is the world my dad grew up in. He was taught that fathers work hard to provide for the family. Saying "I love you" was not in the job description.

In addition, my dad was constantly told to keep quiet. My grandpa had had a heart attack in his thirties, when my dad was a toddler. Because Grandpa needed his sleep while at home in recovery, my dad was constantly told to quiet down.

Then around age seven, my dad developed a habit of getting sore throats. His protective parents (he was the only son and the baby of the family) kept him home from school and pampered him with presents, reinforcing his desire to play hooky.

Thus, my dad not only inherited my grandpa's workaholic lifestyle but also learned to keep to himself, holding his emotions deep inside.

As my brother and I were growing up, my dad worked hard to provide for us, showing his love mainly through buying us things. (Christmases were always overloaded with stuff.) He usually came home from work after we had eaten dinner. I know he wanted to be a good dad. We did things together like Indian Princesses, a father-daughter campout group. He attended my sporting events when he could. He often told me he loved me and was proud of me, but he didn't know how to emotionally connect beyond that. He was never shown how. And of course, I didn't know how to connect with him either.

My mom grew up the middle of three girls. (Her brother, Rob, was born fifteen years later.) She grew up in New York, and her dad took the train into the city every day, not getting home until after the girls were asleep. He was never affectionate and never said "I love you." My mom says the first time her dad even kissed her was when she was twenty-eight years old and going through therapy.

At the awkward age of fourteen, my mom moved from Michigan to Pasadena, California. At the time, her family didn't have much money, so my mom resorted to making her own clothes. She was teased profusely. This could have been manageable had she received the proper support at home, but there was no reinforcement of love from a distant father. Thus her insecurities remained.

As I grew up, my mom was always very productive. With a strong Type A personality, she was great at multi-tasking and taking charge. She had learned from a young age to fend for herself. Because of this, I learned to keep quiet. Mom always took care of everything. I usually just went with the flow, not confident in my own desires or opinions. I know she was just trying to be a good mother. She didn't work until my brother, James, and I were well into elementary school so she could be there for us in our developing years. She was there with us through soccer, piano, volleyball, and so forth, but sometimes we can't escape the tendencies that our past has created.

Because of my mom's past hurts, she looked for approval in appearances.

Everything was always neat and orderly on the outside, because that's how she was taught life had to be. There were diets, shopping sprees, and beauty treatments, totally "normal" for Newport Beach. The house always looked perfect for guests. A clean home is a good thing, but not when it causes you stress or anxiety, or a fear of things not being perfect. Watching all this taught me something about approval: It comes from looking great on the outside.

Our Spirits Speak

Now, let me pause to say my parents are amazing. I love and honor my mom and dad so much that it was very hard for me to write some of these things. They were gracious enough to let me share in order to make a point.

I was blessed with parents who showed an incredible about of love to me and my younger brother, James. It's just that when we are young, our spirits are very sensitive. We pick up things on things that cannot be seen—the unspoken things, the spirit things—which is why I want so desperately to be healed.

I know no matter how much I try to say the right things, to be a good friend, wife, or mother, I'll always hurt people if I'm not whole inside. My words may say one thing, but my spirit will say another. If I'm insecure about who I am, my children and others around me will pick up on it. I will try to love, but I'll be too self-focused to give that deep kind of love we all crave. My mind will always be distracted by fears of what people think and thoughts about myself.

Mom and Dad were never abusive in any way, and looking on the surface, nothing in my childhood points to the reasons behind the eating disorders. But I knew if I wanted to be whole, I had to dig. The more I dug, the more I realized how active the devil has been in planting seeds. He used my mother's insecurities to make me feel insecure. He used the fact that my dad was never shown how to be a dad to also make me feel insecure. I had picked up the spirit things and was left lacking confidence.

Common Themes

While everyone's family history is different, there are usually common themes in the family lives of those who have an eating disorder. There is often a lack of emotional, spiritual, or physical support, making us feel isolated, not fully connected to the family. In some families, feelings are not verbally expressed, making it difficult to communicate freely, openly, and effectively. Instead, we become people-pleasers, learning all the ways that make our parents happy in order to earn their love. We avoid disagreements and therefore become unaware of our own opinions.

We may be applauded for being good students or being independent and responsible. In this case we may feel forced to grow up too fast. We shove down our need to be taken care of and loved and cling to the independence that has been so applauded. Because of a lack of emotional support, we end up having difficulty expressing our emotions verbally. Instead, we try not to rock the boat, quietly dealing with our own thoughts.

In recovery, I found all of these things to be true in my family life. I tried to satisfy my desires for approval by other means, like getting good grades or playing the piano for others so they would praise my skill. I also sought to make everything look neat and orderly on the outside. In second grade, my teacher gave me a character award for being "orderly." I proudly accepted it and attributed it to the way I cleaned and organized my desk.

When this longing for approval progressed into anorexia, I found myself complaining about my weight or what I had eaten. I longed for someone to say, "Jessica, what are you talking about? You're so skinny. Look at you compared to me. Your legs are tiny." I remember standing in front of the mirror with my friend saying I had a big stomach. I pushed it out as far as I could. Then she pushed hers out saying, "Jessica, that's nothing! Look at this!" It secretly brought me comfort to see that her stomach was bigger than mine. I thrived on these comparisons and compliments, but the feelings of approval hinged on the wrong things: my appearance and accomplishments.

Despite your family history, you have the power to break free from generational patterns. You have the opportunity to put an end to them once and for all by aggressively going after the lies and replacing them with the truth. Your approval is not found in what people think of you. It's not found in being perfect or not making mistakes. It's not in having a clean house, a perfect outfit or a perfect body. It's in God alone.

As you heal, the roots of rejection will keep you looking for approval in all the wrong places. Be on guard against searching for approval from others. Instead, know that Daddy God is the only one whose opinion matters. He is madly in love with you and is enthralled by your beauty.

Lastly, your hope cannot rest in the decision to go on a diet. I remember making many promises to myself in the dressing room. I often bought something that was a little tight with the hope that I would lose weight. I also kept clothes in my closet that were too small, vowing to one day fit into them again. Placing your hope in losing weight is a fleeting desire that brings only temporary feelings of satisfaction. Instead, rest your hope in Him alone. Your relationship and nearness to Him is the only thing that will ever consistently satisfy.

CHAPTER 16

REJECTION, SHAME, AND EYE CONTACT

MY counselor pointed out that I rarely made eye contact. This was an outward manifestation of a deep-seated lie. What was the lie? When did it take root? I had to know so I could come out of agreement with it and replace it with God's truth.

When did I stop looking people in the eye? Was I young? Was it when I started lying? I got to be a good liar. No. I think it was before that. I think it was when I stopped being seen.

I remember feeling as if I wasn't seen in elementary school. It was pretty cool at first. I could disappear into the classroom and go on daydreaming away the hours. I already knew how to do school, so my grades were never affected.

Disappearing allowed me to observe the world without getting hurt by it because even at the Christian school people got hurt. Best friends broke up, kids called each other names, and cute guys liked other girls. I didn't want any of that, so I just stayed on the outside. I wasn't a loner. In fact, people always told me I was a leader. I had tons of friends. I could influence. However, I felt as if I was in my own world. I felt different.

Hiding inside myself was the only way I knew how to live. The liar loved keeping me isolated. He would pick on me with lies that sounded like my own thoughts. If I misheard a teacher and answered a question the wrong way, the liar would say, "Stupid. Now everyone thinks you're stupid."

I recall a specific situation in first grade where I asked the teacher if I could use the bathroom. I thought she told me to wait, so I held it. When I couldn't take it any longer, I sheepishly approached her again, "*Now* may I use the bathroom?" "I already said you could," she replied with a smile that said, "Oh, you poor child." I was mortified. I felt so stupid for having to hold it that whole time for no reason. I cursed myself for being so stupid and making a mistake. In counseling, I went back and told seven-year-old me that it was OK to make mistakes.

Believing Lies at a Young Age

Looking into my past helped me see that when I was young, instead of believing that I had a voice, or that adults and others understood me, listened to me, or delighted in me, I believed the liar. The liar had chained a very specific pack of his lies around my ankles: you're shy, you're stupid, you're not cool, you're good at a lot of things but not really great at anything, you're misunderstood, you're awkward, you're weird, you're not seen.

These were circumstances that turned my little soul into vulnerable liar-food:

Circumstance 1: Dad's never home for dinner. He's at the office late, so he can't be involved in my life. Mom runs the show. She told him to take me out to dinner. He tries. But he doesn't get me. And I want to be close, but I don't know how. The lies bite down, and their feeding sounds like, "Dad doesn't know you. He doesn't understand you. You are not really seen. It's easier to just shut your mouth."

Circumstance 2: Mom's always on the phone. Other people seem to be more important than me. "I am not seen," the lies say. (They use the first person to fool me into thinking it's me.)

Circumstance 3: Whenever I try to share with Mom, I get cut off, usually by the ringing phone or by her trying to finish my sentences. I get frustrated. So I just stop trying. I am not heard. So I am not seen. Just shut your mouth.

Circumstance 4: Mom's ability to multitask makes me feel as if I never have her full attention. There's always mail. Nodding a forced, "Ah, that sounds great honey," means she wasn't really listening. Her mouth says one thing, but everything else—body, tone, eyes, spirit—say something completely different. I am misunderstood. I am not listened to. I might as well keep my mouth shut. I am not seen.

Circumstance 5: There's a picture of me that was taken in Mexico when I was eleven. I'm holding an iguana. I'm in my bathing suit. My thighs look big. "You shouldn't be seen," the lies say as they devour my spirit.

But I like iguanas. So I rip off my legs and put the picture on my door. I don't want the real me to be seen. Just the parts I like.

Circumstance 6: My best friend in elementary school is cooler, prettier, and skinnier than I am. She knows things about the world. She makes fun of my Christian music. I try to defend it, but her words hurt. I've never heard of the band Ace of Base. I'm just a dorky private-school girl. I am not cool or accepted, so I am not seen.

Circumstance 7: My best friends in junior high are cooler, prettier, and skinnier than I am. They have bigger boobs. The boys like those girls more than they like me. I feel like a tag-along. I am not seen.

Circumstance 8: My best friend in high school is cooler, prettier, skinner, and more popular than I am. Everybody calls her on the phone. I usually have to call her to find out what's going on. I am not seen.

Lies, lies, lies. Lies that sounded like my own thoughts. If you think a certain way for long enough, you have no way of recognizing that what you're thinking is not right. The devil is not stupid. He's been getting better and better at lying since the beginning of time. He's after your sense of worth.

Early Memories of Not Being Seen

I am under the table.

I am three years old.

I just got in trouble for something, like pushing my baby brother over, and I am supposed to be on time-out in my room. But I'm not in my room anymore. I sneaked downstairs, craftily undetected by my parents, and am now in the living room (a good place for kids to hide because it's so fancy). The funny thing is, the end table I'm under has legs so tall that I'm not hidden. And I know that. Actually, I want to be found.

I'm sitting on my foot, because by now I really have to go potty, but I stubbornly sit, standing my ground. Mad and with mad tears welling in my eyes. Wanting to be found, but hiding. (Hello! Does anybody love me?) And they're not finding me. They don't care. I am invisible. I don't exist. I can't even get attention for leaving my time-out spot.

It's funny to think back on this situation and realize I still sometimes do something similar today. When I'm feeling depressed or lonely, instead of being vocal, I sometimes withdraw and hope my husband notices and digs me out. My stubbornness wants him to feel bad for me, even to the point where he may ask, "What's wrong?" and I say, "Nothing," hoping he'll dig a little more. I get bitter if he doesn't. What a horrible way to go through life.

Despite what I think, people cannot read my thoughts. Some might be more discerning than others, but I can't expect others to read my thoughts. How do they know they've hurt me or that I am hurting unless I tell them? I've got to be open. Pride will keep me hidden. It will keep me holding onto unforgiveness, sitting in the pity party, and clutching the idea that I am the victim. It will make me mad at my husband for no reason at all. How is he supposed to know that I'm sad, or what battles I've been facing in my mind? I have to be open.

Feeling Outside of the Circle

Mom says she always tried to give me more attention when James was born. She was worried I'd feel rejected. She purposely only had two of us so she could have enough love and time to go around. Having suffered for years with chronic middle-child syndrome, she did not want a middle child.

Our babysitter used to worry that James didn't get enough attention. Mom said babies don't notice things like that. Toddlers named Jessica do. Toddlers named Jessica need extra care, because for some reason they think mom loves baby brother more. For some reason Jessica also thinks she is on the outside of the family and baby brother is on the inside. I saw it happen. He was born right into the inside of the family. Me? I don't know how I got here. Maybe I was brought in from somewhere else, like a baby train. Maybe these aren't my parents.

James fit in. He was a product of a marriage between a mom and a dad. And so was I, but for some reason I was jealous. Somebody must have been whispering, "He's a threat. He's come to take the attention of your parents. He belongs. You don't. They'll listen to him. They can't hear you."

Somebody must have been whispering. Otherwise why would I feel this? Even remember feeling this? Why was I so jealous? So bitter toward him?

Later I learned that I was conceived outside of wedlock. Hmmm . . . I guess there's a reason why God established marriage. His way of doing things works. It is how the universe is supposed to function. Doing things outside of His will gives the enemy an open door into our lives.

The lies were there, and I faithfully believed them. "Don't bother looking up, Jessica. They can't see you anyway. They pay more attention to him." I was very independent.

Later Memories

I'm a sophomore in college. An Alpha Phi at the University of San Diego. At the top of my game, I am skinny. I drink a lot well. My "Lil' Sis," the new pledge who is now under my drinking discipleship, is telling me a story at a house party in South Mission Beach. We're standing in the kitchen, and she's really excited about what she's telling me. I'm listening but looking out the window into nothing. I glance back up at her eyes until I get uncomfortable again and find a spot on the corroded counter for my eyes to rest on.

"Look at her!" Another girl tells me.

Wow. What? I thought. *O, yeah. Look at her. Holy crap! People notice eye contact?* I didn't even realize I wasn't looking at the new pledge.

The other girl was standing next to us and had noticed my wandering eyes, and now I'm trying to gather up enough willpower to keep my eyes on the storyteller's. *O God, I think they're crossing. Are my eyes crossed? My mouth hurts. Do I look interested? I feel like I don't look interested. Should I blink? Ahh! She knows I'm faking. I can't do this. O crap. Now I'm really not listening…*

Beyond Eye Contact

I can't remember when I stopped looking people in the eye, but I know it is a sign of something deeper—a fear of rejection that led me to feel shame about the real me. I had believed the lies that I was not seen or heard. I therefore believed that nobody cared to see or hear the real me. *There must be something wrong with me,* I thought. Soon I didn't even want to be seen. It was too uncomfortable, and I felt far too vulnerable to connect with people, to look them in the eye and let them see me.

The rituals associated with the eating disorders allowed me to distance myself from feelings that seemed unmanageable. These feelings were both buried in past events and fresh in my daily life. And not looking people in the eye made me feel safe. If they couldn't see me, I could keep on being who I wanted them to think I was.

In hiding, I forgot who I was. There were walls between every relationship.

And I couldn't even make stinking eye contact with people. *They don't care to see me anyway. And what they see, they really won't like. Besides, it's just easier to shut up and be agreeable. That way nobody gets hurt and people will like me.*

I didn't realize that I was hiding, that I thought I was misunderstood, or that I had lost all sense of who I was. The lies had been in my head for so long that I didn't know anything different. I always made sure everything looked great on the outside. I was friendly, a good student, and very responsible. But that didn't matter when my insides were disconnected.

There are many people walking around like this. Our brokenness is not often obvious. I knew that I wanted deep friendships. I remember wondering if other people felt distant the way I felt. But it sure didn't seem like it. It seemed as if everyone else connected with each other.

And all this came about in a therapy session when I couldn't look my counselor in the eye. I just wanted out, to go somewhere comfortable, to avoid confrontation and take the easy way out.

The Root of Rejection

Many of us suffer the effects of rejection. When we have been denied love, we feel discarded, unlovable, and unworthy to receive love from God and others. No matter how much someone may tell us they love us, deep down the lies whisper back, "No, they don't. They're just saying that to make you feel better. They don't really want to get close to you." This is how the liar steals the truth. Remember, his goal is to destroy you.

In *Ministering Freedom to the Emotionally Wounded*, Chris Hayward includes a chapter on "Overcoming Rejection." According to Hayward, rejection manifests in our lives in four main ways: fear of rejection, rejection of God, rejection of self, and rejection of others.

With the fear of rejection, we want everyone to like us. If they don't, they'll reject us. We sabotage our relationships, rejecting others before they can reject us. We find it's much easier to not get too involved than to have to worry that people will stop liking us for whatever reason. This self-preservation helps us feel in control.

With self-rejection, we determine that somehow, for some reason, we do not fit in. We therefore attack who we really are to become the person we believe will be liked and accepted by everybody. Self-rejection is heard in the negative thoughts we speak over ourselves every day.

Self-rejection is also the same as rejection of God, because we are God's children, made in His image. If we reject the person He created us to be and who God says we are, we call God a liar. God calls us beautiful, fearfully and wonderfully made, and to think anything less means we reject His Word, and by association, Him. We also reject God because we feel He has rejected us. We therefore stay away because we believe He will hurt us or simply not protect us. We don't trust His intentions and decide that we need to protect ourselves.

All of this comes on us because the enemy wants us to live in fear and mistrust. He wants us to cast blame on others and sever the divine relationships we were created to live for.

What's the solution? The spirit of adoption. The roots of rejection are severed when we grab hold of the truth that we are accepted into Jesus's royal family. Adopted in through His blood! You are not on the outside of the circle. You've been adopted right in. First John 3:1 says, "How great is the love the Father has lavished on us, that we should be called children of God! And that is what we are!"

Ask God for His fatherly affirmation of who you are as His daughter or son. Every child needs to hear their father saying, "You're mine, and I love you just as you are." Read through the New Testament letters, such as Colossians and Ephesians. Grab hold of your new identity as His beloved and accepted child. Soak your thoughts in the truth of who God is and who you are in Jesus.

Know that He is faithful. Abandon doubt. Declare that even though you may have felt abandoned by God, He has never left you. The enemy wanted you to believe that God ignored your cries, but God says He has heard you and is answering. All He wants is you. The lies have created walls and false filters that twist our perception of what is really going on. They make it difficult to hear the truth. That's why we need to cling to His Word and believe it despite our experience. The truth is, God never left you.

To Whom Have You Given Power to Determine Your Worth?

It was the fear of rejection that kept me from looking at my counselor, Jane. I was deeply ashamed and didn't want to be seen. If looking into someone's eyes shames us, we have given others the power to determine our worth. We are ashamed of what we have done, and we think, *If they really saw me, they'd be disgusted by me.* We fear being exposed because we fear that people will permanently reject and abandon us. We've entrusted our soul to the wrong people.

Only God can determine your worth. You are His beloved child. His very own. Out of the bazillion things He could be doing, He chooses to spend time with you every day. That gives you an incredible amount of worth. If the president decided to come have dinner at your house, you'd feel as if you must be something pretty special and important. Well, the King of the universe can't get enough of you! Can you receive that? He's right next to you, adoring who you are.

Healing is not easy. It's a process. And it must start somewhere, even if it's just with eye contact. I still have to practice that. I have to make sure I'm giving others my full attention, because my mind can be so preoccupied with myself. *Do I have food in my teeth? Are there other conversations going on that I'm missing out on? Does she like me? Man, I feel fat. Does my outfit look OK?* If I don't get my eyes off of myself, the worry and insecurity . . . they'll eat me alive.

Instead, I choose to refuse this illegitimate shame and determine that my worth is in God alone, and He thinks I'm the most amazing thing He's ever seen. Once I'm able to rest secure in this identity, I have no problem connecting with people. I know I have something to give and something to receive. I can give my friends my full attention, look into their eyes, and hear what they are saying. I can truly connect.

CHAPTER 17

LYING AND STEALING

"**H**OW did it get so easy? Now it's hard to stop. I lie when I don't even need to." This revelation came when I noticed myself lying about little things, like saying a pair jeans cost me $65 when they really cost me $69.99. This really bothered me. Why was I lying? It makes me feel fake. But I want to be real!

Lying had become a part of my everyday life. When I was anorexic, lies got me through the day. They kept my secret safe. When I was bulimic, the lies got more creative. I remember most trips to the grocery store included fake phone conversations near the register. I hoped to have people believe that all the junk food was for a party, not just for me. It helped me feel normal.

I even stole food to trick myself into believing that none of this was happening. I'd open a bag of candy or dried fruit, eat some, and then sneak it back on the shelves. I also stole laxatives. Using laxatives was a way of lying to myself about getting better. I didn't make myself throw up as much when I was using them, so I felt like I was doing a good job. It also helped that I could tell my counselor I had gone a whole week without purging. Lies, lies, lies. The truth is I had to undergo excruciatingly painful stomach cramps due to laxative abuse. I was destroying my intestines. I was ashamed and I was lonely.

Because I know lying can be a stronghold, I am very sensitive to being truthful, especially to myself. As mentioned in a previous chapter, it's easy to lie to myself: *It's no big deal to steal that candy. No one will know.* The mind will justify what the heart desires. It's how we hide our ugliness, but it's not OK.

Once during recovery I opened a bag of marshmallows in a store, ate some as I shopped, and then put them back. I didn't want to pay for them and then have to deal with the whole bag sitting in my cupboards. Later I confessed to a friend what I had done. I went back to the store and told them that I had gotten marshmallows but they weren't rung up. They gladly let me pay. It wasn't the whole truth, but it was a start.

A few years later, when I was dating Jesse and dealing with some difficult emotions, I found myself in a grocery store wanting to calm my nerves with food. I picked out a cookie from the glass case and ate it without paying. Later I felt so guilty that I told Jesse. I then went back to the store and told them the whole embarrassing truth. I told them that I was recovering from eating disorders and that sometimes I resorted to old habits and that I had stolen a cookie and wanted to pay for it. The customer service girl looked at me surprised but was glad to help me in the healing process. She let me pay for the cookie without calling security. It was embarrassing but freeing at the same time. I had let a stranger in on the dark secrets of my heart, and the light set me free from guilt and shame.

Lying was also something I had to get free from. In my first year of marriage, I went shopping for Christmas decorations since we finally had our own home to decorate. I spent $80. I thought Jesse would think that was a crazy amount of money to spend on decorations that we didn't need. As I drove away from the store, I thought about telling him I spent $40. I caught myself subtly formulating the lie and then asked myself why I wanted to lie. I had to find the root.

I realized that I wanted to lie because I wanted him to see me as a wise shopper. If I only spent $40, he'd be proud of me for finding such great deals and being such a creative and resourceful homemaker. What a lie! I knew that if I lied to Jesse, it wouldn't be me he'd be proud of but a make-believe me. A *me* I made up. If I wanted him to really know me, I had to be truthful always, even if it meant facing fears.

I had to face the fear that he might be upset with me spending so much money. I had to understand that if he was upset it didn't mean he didn't love me. It just meant we had some differences to sort through. We'd have to discuss our different perspectives. While men tend to enjoy things for their usefulness, women enjoy things that look pretty. We'd have to come to a compromise. That's it. It has nothing to do with love or acceptance. Disagreeing does not mean rejection of me.

I ended up telling him the truth, and he didn't bat an eye. He trusted me to be wise with our money, and while he may not have thought we needed some of the things I bought, he let me enjoy decorating.

Being honest prevented a wall from going up in our marriage. I had protected our unity simply by admitting the truth of the situation.

Lying is hiding. Like failing to maintain eye contact, it puts up walls between other people and the real me. In this situation I feared rejection and therefore tried to cover up who I really was in order to gain favor and acceptance.

What pieces are keeping you from being whole? Are you hiding just to avoid confrontation, just to stay neutral so everyone likes you? So you can please everyone? Are you lying or stealing so you can appear to have it all together?

People long for real people. As I said in the beginning, that's why people like juicy gossip, the front story on the back story. We're not content with celebrities being perfect, so we dig up their junk. We want to know what's really going on in people's lives, even if it's for the wrong reason. That human characteristic of desiring closeness with people was put inside all of us by a triune God who made us in His image of perfect fellowship.

So, the next time you find yourself wanting to lie or steal, ask yourself why. Then, know that the truth will set you free to be truly known. The truth will help you receive the love you're trying to earn. You can't earn love be creating someone you're not. It's no wonder we feel lonely. We don't let anyone love us. Let's tear down the walls and be loved.

CHAPTER 18

FAMILY AND FORGIVENESS

THE root of rejection is also broken through forgiveness. As I dove into the past and began recovering memories and emotions, I also uncovered the realization that I needed to forgive a few people, mainly my parents. I thought I had forgiven them, but the returning memories still had bite. Although I always defended them in counseling, Jane encouraged me to be honest. I was hurt. I needed to voice my pain.

As kids, we grow up believing that our parents are superhuman, incapable of making mistakes. But that doesn't mean that we haven't been hurt by them, even if it's unintentional. I know my parents were the best parents they could be, but everyone comes with baggage. So on top of raising a brood of kidlets, they were also fighting their own personal battles.

Growing up, we have no concept of this. That's why it hurts so much when we feel neglected or mistreated. We're not mature enough to realize that our parents go through things as well. Instead, we get mad at them for not being perfect, or we think there must be something wrong with us.

Writing Letters

In order to help with the healing process, I wrote two letters, one to my mom and one to my dad. I did not intend on sending them. I wanted to have complete freedom to unleash any pain from the past, without feeling as if I had to defend them. Forgiveness does not mean you ignore the situation. It means you face it, and then offer mercy instead of holding the person ransom.

Writing provided a good release. I wasn't angry, just hurt, and by not defending them in the letter I was able to release the poison that had been festering. They didn't need to know most of the stuff I was hurt about. I had no intention of making them feel bad. I gave them back to God and trusted that He would deal with any patterns in their lives that needed to be dealt with. They didn't owe me an apology. (This is a hard realization to face.) I was not in charge of their actions, only mine.

So while the letter was helpful, it was by no means a letter about pinning my eating disorder on them. Nobody gets healed through shifting blame. It was simply to voice my feelings. At the end, I forgave them both for the specific things I could remember, in my own time with God. I also had to repent for holding onto unforgiveness for so long. It was hard, but it felt good to let go.

Freedom to Share and Repent

After forgiving them, I felt comfortable enough to have my parents come to a counseling session. With the pride and bitterness squashed, I was able to be open. They knew bits and pieces of what I had been going through, but not the details. Praise God, I have very accepting and forgiving parents who would do anything to help me. You may not have that luxury. I know some girls who squirm at the thought of ever telling their parents. It's simply unimaginable to them.

Sharing with your parents may or may not be a safe option right now. Your counselor will help with that, but it's ultimately your decision. Remember, baby steps. First be open with someone you can trust. Trust God to lead you every step of the way. You can't control other people's reactions, but you can control how free you are going to be. You can decide to forgive.

Forgiveness also freed me up to repent. Pride and self-preservation were no longer actively keeping me blind. I recognized how I had hurt my parents. Humility washed over me, and I was able to repent for years of rebellion and selfishness. It was still a little awkward, but the freedom was there. Our relationship was being restored.

I also repented for how I had judged them. The Bible says you will be judged to the measure in which you judge. I was keeping myself in bondage (judgment) because of my judgments towards others. I judged them when I focused on their faults. Once I repented to God for judging them, I experienced a whole new level of freedom.

The Key of Forgiveness

Forgiveness is an amazing key. If we choose to use it, it can unlock us from the chains that bind us to past and present wounds, setting us free to walk in an abundant future. "But," you may be thinking, "they don't deserve to be forgiven." Make a choice to forgive them anyway. Forgiveness is not a feeling. It's a choice. Choose to speak: "I forgive ___for ____ . They don't owe me an apology. I release them from my grip and give them back to You, God." Let it all go. Write a few letters like I did. It will feel so good.

The decision to forgive sets you free. The decision not to forgive locks you in a prison of pain, holding you back from all the joy and happiness God has in store for you. By forgiving my parents, I silenced the accuser's lies, freeing me up to enjoy them and be enjoyed. Holding onto unforgiveness does not gain the revenge you desire. It only ends up hurting you, often leaving the other person totally unaware of the situation.

After forgiving my parents, I noticed myself getting less bitter and closed off when I went to visit them. I got less annoyed at things that used to bother me. Today I look forward to spending time with them or chatting with them on the phone, and I am able to be completely open and free. Finally the walls are down, allowing for an amazing exchange of love.

It may not be immediately possible for the people you need to forgive to be in your life. There may be people you need to forgive that you actually need to stay away from. But through forgiveness, the chains to that person will be cut off, and you can fully engage with the ones you want to be with.

Forgiveness with Siblings

I also had to forgive and ask forgiveness from by younger brother, James. Although we were buddies growing up, it was definitely a love-hate relationship. I was always somehow threatened by him and felt he was getting more attention than I was. (The enemy was loudly lying.) I used to call him stupid because it made me feel better.

Even in college, I compared myself to him. When we both came back to the Lord, I was about to be a senior and he a freshmen, both at USD. James received several prophetic words about his future that had me feeling jealous. Comparison and competition had marked my life growing up, and it was putting distance between us.

Especially when it came to looks. I was always given attention for my looks when I was a young teen. But when James matured, everyone thought he should be a model, with his naturally bleach-blond hair and big blue eyes. I suddenly felt very plain, with brown hair and hazel eyes, hidden in my brother's shadow. I was insecure about my weight and thought he was embarrassed to be seen with me. Lies, lies, lies. Lies that had to be brought into the open.

I forgave my brother for all the specific things I could remember being bitter about: for being cuter, for not having to worry about his weight, for getting away with things. (It was not necessary to speak these things to his face since he was unaware of my secret comparisons). Then I made the important step of repentance. I repented to him for being distant and selfish. I wasn't a good sister, especially in high school when all I cared about was my happiness. We acknowledged the elephant in the room, and we were finally able to begin building a friendship based on love and truth. It's so much fun to be free!

Forgiving the Ones You Compare Yourself To

As I learned more about forgiveness, I realized that any time I felt bitter, it was because of unforgiveness. I compared myself to my best friend all the time. I was jealous because she got to walk or ride her bike to work every day and was in better shape than I was. I had no reason to be angry with her. She had not wronged me. But because I thought it wasn't fair that she didn't seem to struggle to keep weight off or resist cookies, I held bitterness in my heart toward her. I had to forgive her, too.

I had to forgive anytime I felt myself getting mad at others for being skinny or not worrying about what they ate or for making comments about food or weight in my presence. I had to say, "What's going on with them has nothing to do with me. They're not trying to rub anything in my face. I forgive them for hurting me, even though it was unintentional." That way, I freed myself up to love them and be loved by them. What a glorious freedom!

Our negative or competitive thoughts toward others must be brought into the light. When things are buried, they have a way of growing roots—roots of fear that bear the fruit of bitterness and shame (which is actually pride). Shame keeps us from sharing, and the cycle continues. We must break the cycle and restore relationships through forgiveness.

Who do you need to forgive? Sometimes you may have to forgive some people over and over again, but that's OK. Do not let any hatred or bitterness brew in your heart. It will eat you up inside and keep you from gaining the freedom you desire. So go ahead. Forgive. Forgive God, forgive yourself, forgive your family, forgive your friends, forgive those who have hurt you. Forgive seventy times seven. It will feel so good.

PART IV

THE TRANSFORMED MIND

I used to think I could never be free, because unlike an alcoholic, a person with an eating disorder can never be free from food. I would always be tormented by it, have to eat it, buy it, and cook it. Throughout recovery I have learned that I can be free because it wasn't an addiction to food that was ruling my life, it was an addiction to negative or false ways of thinking.

Fear-based mentalities ran my life. I had to transform my mind. Let me show you how I broke free.

CHAPTER 19

OUR INHERITANCE

LIFE is hard. Nobody else understands. I can't be perfect anyway. This prison isn't so bad. After all, I'm just a sinner.

This was pretty much my reality before God woke me up. I believed that I was the victim. The world and its ways were bigger than God and His ways. Fighting bulimia was an endless pursuit. I wasn't sure if I could ever be free.

My perceived reality was based on a lie. In healing I discovered the true reality—the kingdom reality. When Jesus said, "Pray like this," "Your kingdom come, Your will be done, on earth as it is in heaven," it wasn't just a nice prayer about the future (see Matthew 6:10). He was declaring that God's kingdom, His way of doing things, would be manifested on earth right now, not when we "get to heaven." He tells us the kingdom of heaven is at hand. It's within reach in the supernatural realm all around us. Our job is to make it manifest in the earthly realm.

There's no bondage in heaven, right? That means it's not God's will for there to be bondage here on earth. His will is that it would be "on earth as it is in heaven". And He's given us the keys to unlock our doors, to fling them wide open, and to have heaven's reality invade this one. But we must see the keys, His perspective, in order to use them.

We need to know the rights and privileges of being a son or daughter of the Most High God. Becoming a Christian isn't about getting a ticket into heaven. Because of His love, believing in the one true God, Jesus Christ, means that we have the opportunity to see from His perspective, to see what the Father in heaven is doing (see John 5:20). He loves us so much that He abolished those things that were keeping us separated from Him, allowing for complete unity with His Spirit and complete transference of heaven's reality into our reality. Jesus said, "Everything I have [the entire inheritance of the kingdom] is yours" (Luke

15:31). You get the keys to supernatural healing, to divine identity and purpose, and to deep life-giving relationships with God, your family, and your friends. We receive His perspective, His mind, and His heart.

As an heir to the kingdom, I realized that I no longer had to live as a victim of circumstance and bondage. Circumstance and bondage became my victims. Ephesians 2:6 says, "And God raised us up with Christ and seated us with Him in the heavenly realms in Christ Jesus." I am not under the weight of the world. I am seated high above it, next to Him who sits on the throne, because He has called me His friend. Who else would He want sitting next to Him than His best friend?

Therefore when I pray, I pray from a place of authority and certainty, not from a place of, "O, I hope He hears me up there." No. We're right next to Him, and our prayers avail much (James 5:16)! We are righteous because of grace, no longer beggars, but sons!

Because He has adopted me as a daughter, I have authority. I am a member of God's royal family. "His divine power has given us everything we need for a godly life through our knowledge of him who called us by his own glory and goodness. Through these he has given us his very great and precious promises, so that through them you may participate in the divine nature, having escaped the corruption in the world caused by evil desires" (2 Peter 3-4). In Him, I lack nothing.

No Longer Sinners

When you are able to walk in this reality, your perceived bondage will be defeated. When we believe that Jesus is the Son of God, and when we believe in the power of His death and resurrection, we, too, die and rise again. Romans 6:4 says, "We were therefore buried with Him through baptism into death in order that, just as Christ was raised from the dead through the glory of the Father, we too may live a new life."

We are "dead to sin but alive to God in Christ Jesus" (Romans 6:11). Could it be any clearer? We are no longer sinners! We died to sin! Some of you are really struggling with this right now. You've been taught that we'll always sin and that's why we need Jesus. Yes, we do need Jesus, but I believe part of the reason why we have such a problem with sin is because we don't know the truth about who we are. We may sin, sure, but it's not our nature anymore. For, "Those who belong to Christ Jesus have crucified the sinful nature with its passions and desires" (Galations 5:24). Our new nature cannot, I repeat, *cannot*, sin. But how can that be if we still sin? Because sin doesn't come from who we really are. We can only sin when we believe a lie.

By His grace, we are not sinners. We are saints. Calling ourselves a sinner is like putting on a false identity. As my husband says, "If we believe we are just sinners, we will sin by faith." But when we come into a relationship with God through Jesus, we get His full identity, a brand-new nature. Sinning is not something that this new nature can do. Romans 6:1, 6 says, "We died to sin; how can we live in it any longer? . . . because anyone who has died has been freed from sin."

What I Am Tempted by Does Not Define Me

In recovery, there were many times when I let the enemies lies become my identity. When tempted with food I'd think, *Man, what's wrong with me? Why am I so weak? I'm never gonna stop thinking about food. I guess it's just who I am.* But then I realized temptation is not bondage unless I let it be. If I believe that I am a bulimic, then I will act like one. But as soon as I put my identity in Him, and not in my sin, I receive the power to overcome temptation.

The temptation will come, but when it does, it's not because it's a part of me; it's simply because the enemy wants me to believe it is. He'll tempt me with the same thing over and over again so that I think it's a part of my identity. But it's not. And I don't have to agree with the temptation: "No, food won't satisfy my loneliness right now. I am not in bondage to it. You can't fool me. I'm already free!" Every time I disagree with the lies, the temptations get weaker and weaker until one day they will become obsolete.

Many of us still believe we are in the tomb. We've asked God for help, but we're not ready to let go of that burial shroud. We keep putting it back on, thinking it's our identity, thinking it's safer, cozier, or easier. But it's not. It's death. We're afraid of letting go. But fear is simply putting your faith in the wrong truth. As soon as you believe His truth about your identity, the fear will dissolve.

What thoughts are keeping you in bondage? Do you perceive yourself on the losing end of the battle, a victim of circumstance, or just a sinner? The next time you feel trapped under the weight of your eating disorder, picture yourself next to the Father, seated on a throne in the heavenly places. He desires your company you like a best friend. Because of the blood of Jesus, in His eyes, you are royalty, so stop believing any different.

You don't have to give in to the eating disorder anymore because it is not of you. It is not who you are! It is merely a temptation of the enemy that you already have victory over. Put the enemy back in his place declaring the Truth. Know that he is under your foot and is never stronger than you. Fix your eyes on God and know that you are high above it all, with all the inheritance of His power and authority right at your fingertips.

God will not let the enemy tempt you beyond what you can bear (see 1 Corinthians 10:13). No matter how hard it feels to resist, know that victory is just one decision away.

CHAPTER 20

ALL OR NOTHING

IN addition to seeing myself as royalty, I discovered several other ways in which my mind was working against me. There were not only spiritual forces at work but physical ones as well. For instance, when we think the same thought enough times, little grooves begin to form on the surface of our brains. The more often the thought comes, the deeper the groove gets, much like a toboggan traversing the same trail in the snow over and over again. The deeper the trail, the less free you become. If you want to change course, you're going to have to exert some effort.

One trail I discovered myself getting stuck in was the "all or nothing" trail. It was a thought process that kept me bound. In my experience, all-or-nothing looks like this: I eat a cookie. That means I messed up. My day is ruined. I might as well keep on going, eating more cookies to make my mess-up worth it. Feast or famine. Go all in, or starve.

I envied people who could eat just one cookie or order a piece of cake and then stop when they were full. I've watched people do this and hated them for it. They seemed so carefree. Why weren't they thinking about the food? If I ate a piece of cake, I usually ended up looking for the next chance to snag another without acting too suspicious. Then I could make the purge worth it. Either that or I just wouldn't have any at all.

So, how did I move on from this "all or nothing" mentality, this "black or white" thinking? My counselor asked me a good question one day:

"Is the cookie 'good' or 'bad'?"

"Bad," I replied.

"Why?"

"It's not healthy."

"Says who?"

"Everyone knows cookies are bad for you. They're sugary and fattening."

"What if you ate just one occasionally?"

"I dunno."

You see, there was no room for cookies in a healthy diet because in my eyes they were bad. But when I realized one cookie is OK, it's not good or bad, it just is, I could incorporate things like that into my diet without overanalyzing it or thinking I had ruined my entire day. I no longer believed that I was a horrible person for having such little self-control.

This all-or-nothing mentality transferred over into most areas of my life. I was either fat or thin, ugly or pretty, a success or a failure. Most times I fell on the negative end of the spectrum. To me there were no in-betweens. No room for mistakes.

Finding Middle Ground

Recovering from eating disorders is a balance. I have to ditch my all or nothing, black and white thinking, and find middle ground. So instead of saying, "I already messed up today. I'll just keep on going along with the eating disorder and start over tomorrow," I had to realize I could start over every minute—every second. "I ate a cookie, but that's OK. I'm not going to eat ten. I can live with one or two cookies in my stomach." Even if I resorted to purging, this does not set me back to square one. It simply means I have an opportunity to discover how it happened.

Nothing Is Off Limits

One of the best things I did for myself in recovery was to know that no food was off limits. "What?" you may be thinking. "What about cake? That's a sure way to get fat like the rest of America." But I realized that it wasn't the fact that it tasted good that made the cake so tempting, it was that it was off limits. Once I trashed the "good/bad" list, the power of temptation weakened. I could look at that free doughnut at church and say, "I could eat that if I wanted to. But do I really want to?" And if I decide that I want to, I'm not ashamed because I'm not failing or breaking any rules. I'm a free person, and I can eat a doughnut if I want. I can enjoy it instead of stuffing it quickly into my mouth so nobody sees. Nobody's watching anyway. I can also decide that I don't want it. I am free. I can make choices based on what I want, not on what rules and lies tell me.

There have been several studies done on the effects of food deprivation. Whether it be in the case of famine, yo-yo dieting, or an eating disorder, food deprivation leads to rebound eating.

I had lived with the rule that dessert was bad. I tried to stave off the desire for chocolate by eating fruit, but that almost never satisfied my craving and only left me "on the prowl" for more fat-free or "healthy foods." None of it satisfied my craving. Thus, when I let myself have a treat on the weekend, my body went into overload, thinking it would never again be in contact with that dessert. Better eat as much as you can now.

Through the book *Intuitive Eating* by Evelyn Tribole, M.S., R.D., and Elyse Resch, M.S., R.D., F.A.D.A, I learned to slowly let "off limits" food back into my diet. Yesterday was a Tuesday and I was craving chocolate. I honored my body's cravings and went to the store and bought some chocolate covered nuts and pretzels.

The *me* before the healing would have been frantic and out of control, quickly stuffing the chocolates into my mouth and feeling guilty the entire time. But in making peace with food I'm learning to notice how things taste. I've slowed things down, asking myself, does this satisfy my craving? Does it still taste good? If it doesn't, I throw it away. If it does, I let myself enjoy it.

After finishing my small baggie of mixed chocolates (and throwing away the ones I didn't enjoy), I didn't feel guilty. And today I don't feel like I need to make up for it by skipping meals or working out extra hard. I'm making peace with food. And surprisingly, my weight is stable.

I used to be afraid that if I listened to my body instead of the rules, I would only crave unhealthy things and get fat and out of control. But the more I listened to my body, I realized that sometimes what I truly craved was an apple or grilled veggies. That's because the effects of deprivation apply to any type of food. I recall a three-day hiking trip through the Grand Canyon where we ate only trail food like protein bars. When we finally returned to the top, I remember having an intense craving for a big chicken salad with lots of greens. My body knows what it needs!

Remember, food is not good or bad, it just is. Begin to make peace with food. You will be surprised at how much less you crave certain things. You will be less anxious at social gatherings. Learning to honor your body will set you free from guilt and "all or nothing" thinking.

CHAPTER 21

FROM APATHY AND CONDEMNATION TO CONVICTION

IN learning to avoid the all-or-nothing mentality, I discovered another set of lies requiring attention: the voices of apathy and condemnation. This happened when trying to "lighten up" and "eat just one" turned into bingeing.

Apathy

Apathy sounds like this: "Just this last time, Jessica. You deserve it. You've had a long day. Lighten up. Just have a cookie. Now that you've had one, why don't you just finish them off? If you just give in, these tormenting thoughts will finally leave you alone. You know you want to. You don't have to throw up. You want to be free, right? You're free to eat them all!"

Out of apathy, I agreed with these lies, pretended it wasn't a problem, and refused to take responsibility. I didn't want to deal with it anymore. I knew that eating all the cookies wasn't freedom. I'd been there before, but I was tired. So I'd give in. This inevitably led to another set of lies: "Now you have to throw up." Whether or not I won that battle, condemnation always came right in to join the party.

Condemnation

Condemnation sounds like this: "How could you eat so much?! You're so stupid! You knew you would end up feeling worse. Why'd you do it? It was not worth it, and you knew it. You're never gonna stop. You'll never be free. You're just gonna keep getting fatter. You are such a screw-up!" Many of my journal entries are laced with these comforting words.

Here's the funny thing: Apathy and condemnation both come from the same source. They have the same father! They're the voice of the enemy. One minute he's saying, "Go ahead. Pick at that gallon of ice cream. You can eat just a little. Lighten up. You deserve it." The next, it's "Just a little more. It's no big deal. It'll satisfy your longing and make you feel better." Finally, his condemning voice shouts, "How could you? You're so disgusting! You're a pig, and you know it!"

Yes, that same voice that lured you into the mess is now scolding you for doing it. It's these lies that make us feel trapped, as if we're going crazy.

The Answer

The answer to these warring thoughts is repentance and grace. It's conviction, not condemnation. It's "God, I'm sorry. Thank You for being patient with me. You know my heart is to stop doing this. You know it's my desire. Thank You, God, for still holding me in my mess."

And if you let Him hold you as you're being tempted to keep eating, the feeling of His comfort far surpasses anything food could give you. Letting God comfort you instead of food takes practice, but the more you do it, calling out to Him and telling Him you need a hug, sitting and letting His love come in, the more tangible His comforting arms become. Often it seems that food is a much more tangible route, but God's pleasures are far superior to the pleasures of the world (Psalm 16:11).

Go on a walk—flee—and let Him talk to you. I did this many times in the middle of a binge. I could stop bingeing before I even had to deal with the agonizing thoughts of needing to throw up. If you call on His name, He will answer. I promise. It may take time to discern the way He answers, but He is always near, and He loves you more than you can ever know. He does not withhold love from His kids. Call out to Him. He will give you the strength to fight the apathy and the love to silence condemnation. You can do it!

When Apathy Landed on Me . . . Hard!

Fighting takes energy. I get tired. I want to give up. And there are times when I have given up. One particular time in 2005, I decided I had done a good job. My counselor and I had determined that I was ready to continue healing on my own, with the help of the friends I trusted. Unfortunately, I decided I had fought enough, so I dropped my guard. After all, my friend did tell me I was kicking the devil's brains out.

Remember that season I had, using the Word of God every day like a sword? That was my senior year of college. I had moved out on my own. I couldn't live surrounded by the parties (I was too weak), and I didn't have any Christian friends yet. It was easier to be bulimic in my own house. And actually, as I mentioned before, bulimia got much worse during this time, but it was oddly also getting better. Through God's Word and counseling, I was discovering the lies, the triggers, and the truth.

Even though living on my own revealed to me my greatest weaknesses—as they say, you are who you truly are when nobody's watching—it helped me realize I needed to fight. I built up confidence with the Word of God.

Then I received an encouraging word from God through a friend. He said, "I feel like God's saying to you, 'You're kicking the devil's brains out.'"

"Wow! I am? Sweet! So all that pacing and speaking the truth out loud really did something. Woo-hoo! You hear that devil? God says I am kicking your brains out!"

Needless to say, I left feeling great about myself. But then I went off to grad school to pursue a certificate in campus ministry. My focus shifted from fighting the monster to studying, doing homework, and taking tests. I'm good at doing school. I love getting stuff checked off my list, so of course I tackled homework assignments with zeal, finishing before most of my classmates. Not out of competition but more out of a need to feel accomplished.

But all the furious typing of papers and chewing on pens also brought with it the abandonment of my arsenal. The weapons I had been so persistently sharpening began to go unused. I found myself again bingeing on everything and anything, usually going after one of my housemate's tasty study snacks. I would sit in front of the computer snacking myself into a Goldfish cracker frenzy only to come crashing down into a pile of sluggish discomfort.

Then I did it. I went into the bathroom in the hall that had a lock on the door. I got into the shower with an empty pitcher and made myself throw up. Just like old times. I remember thinking, *O crap, here I am at grad school still doing this. I thought I'd be done with it by now. Am I ever gonna be over this?* But I kept on going. The first time in a new place was always like breaking the seal.

Once I did it and knew I could get away with it, it was much easier to do it again. And again. And again.

Apathy had rolled in to rain on my Sunday best. And it was thick. And miserable. I could see it on my face—ugly, unhealthy, swollen, and tired. I wanted to put a stop to bulimia forever. But this relapse sent me plunging into a major case of "I'm over it" and "just this last time."

I kept denying the fact that I needed help. *I'm in ministry school. People in ministry school can't struggle with something so heinous.* I thought it would stop soon. It didn't. I finally told the woman who was mentoring me at the time. It was embarrassing. We scheduled a meeting with Sarah, a pastor's wife. (O crap. We're calling in the big guns.)

So we met at Sarah's house. She answered the door with a baby in her arms and a six-year-old daughter running back and forth from the kitchen to the family room to ask mommy questions. Immediately I felt ashamed. Busy mama's gotta take time out to deal with selfish, pathetic me.

So I sat there on the big overstuffed couch, arms crossed, explaining the unhealthy patterns of eating I'd succumbed to over the previous month, of course sparing all the details, downplaying the extent of the symptoms, and not showing any emotion whatsoever.

It's not that I didn't have any emotion. Inside I was all knotted up, full of discontentment, frustration, discomfort, and shame. But outside I was as steady as a comatose college student, stoned, and hashing out my latest endeavors in a monotone. Could I at least muster a tear or something? *Come on, Jessica! Cry! You know you want to! You know you want to just lose it like a little girl crying for Mommy. You know you just want to be held. So why is it so hard to show emotion?*

Luckily Sarah broke the silence with an encouraging mama lecture. She didn't tell me what I wanted to hear. She didn't treat my actions as no big deal. She didn't paste on a fake smile and one of those annoyingly gentle voices and offer me weak solutions. No, she offered the strength of a mother. She told me I needed to figure out who I was. As she bounced her baby back and forth, she asked me to list ten things I liked about who I was. I sat there silent for a while before muttering, "I can draw, I can play the piano, I can write poems, um . . . "

She stopped me. "OK, those are things you can do. I asked what you liked about who you *are*."

I thought. Nothing came.

She explained that I wouldn't do what I was doing to myself if I knew who I was. What are your strengths? What are your character traits? What defines you? Who *are* you?

Silence from me.

She was giving me just what I needed.

Elijah

I told her I felt like Elijah. He was a prophet who lived during the ninth century B.C. He was close to God and constantly in situations where he needed supernatural strength. Once when he was wrongfully accused of killing a widow's son, he prayed for God to put breath back into the boy. And He did! He was able to have faith because of his closeness with God.

He even challenged those who worshiped the gods of Baal to a contest to prove whose God was more powerful. During the competition at Mount Carmel, Elijah asked the prophets to call on their god to bring fire so they could roast their sacrificed bull. Baal never showed up. Then Elijah called to the God of the universe, and fire consumed the altar, which had been soaked with water to make the challenge even more difficult. Victory!

Elijah was probably feeling pretty good right about then. It was in this moment of triumph that Queen Jezebel ordered him killed. Elijah freaked out. "Enough! I can't take it anymore!" And, fearing for his life, he fled.

I felt the way he did. I had been growing in intimacy with the Lord, using the power of His truth to destroy the enemy's schemes. But one more attack, and I fled from His arms. I was tired of fighting, and I just wanted out.

Sarah said the way she had understood that story was that Elijah was running because he had forgotten who he was. All he had to do was look back and see that God had always provided, because he was God's beloved son and God would never leave His son alone. He had no reason to fear Jezebel. What could a mortal do to him?

Sarah gave me an assignment. She said, "I want you to go home and figure out who you are. Every day I want you to ask God to show you an aspect of who you are. Know that He loves you, and He will speak to you."

CHAPTER 22

WHO ARE YOU?

THE next day as I was reading the "confession sheet," I asked God to reveal to me who I was.

September 21, 2005

OK, Lord. Who am I?

I read the verse in Colossians 3:3, "Set your mind on things above, not on earthly things. For you died, and your life is now hidden with Christ in God." I heard God say, "You are hidden with Christ in God."

"What the heck does that mean?"

"You are hidden with Me [Christ] in Me [God]. Jessica, you are not who you see in the mirror. Your body, your face—those are not who you are. They are gifts I have given to you to be a steward over. But they are not who you are. Your life is with Me. Your life is in Me. Your life is only made evident through Me. The other parts of you have died. They are no longer who you are. Your new self is being renewed in the knowledge and image of its Creator. As you come to this knowledge, people will no longer see your body; they'll see Me. We are not separate. The two have become one. So be a faithful steward of your body because I gave it to you to take care of, but you yourself are hidden with Me inside this gift I've given you. When you see yourself in the mirror, look deeper. You and I are there together. We are members of one body."

"Wow, Lord. That's pretty cool."

"When I say that I am enthralled by your beauty, I'm not looking at your body. Your body is lovely to Me, yes. It is My creation, perfect in form, but you are so much more beautiful than that. Your body's got nothing on you!"

When I came in from my run that night, Bethany said, "Jessica, you're so cute. Seriously, just a natural beauty." And then Alli chimed, in saying, "Yeah, even when you sweat, you just have this natural presence about you."

I knew this wasn't me physically. This was God shining out of me. I had been meditating on His goodness, and I felt so full and so light at the same time. And I saw it in the mirror. As I went into the bathroom to shower, I looked in the mirror, and I was glowing. It was a genuine manifestation of the Scripture that talks about beauty coming not from outward adornments but from the heart.

> *"Whoa, Lord," I wrote. "I saw beauty in me tonight like I hadn't seen it in a long while. Thank You, God. You are so good.*
> *"Lord, don't ever stop revealing Yourself to me.*
> *"In You I am free.*
> *"In You I am me."*

"Sure"

As I began to let God define me, I noticed a word in my vocabulary that revealed some of my lingering insecurities: "Sure." "How about this movie? You wanna watch it?" "Sure." "Or what about this one? Does it sound good to you?" "Um, I don't know. Sure." Because I was either uncertain or insecure about my opinions and desires, I used this word to stay safe.

I was unaware of this until one day I asked my friend if she wanted to meet for coffee. "Sure," she said. What does that mean? Does it mean, "Well, I don't really want to, but I guess I could meet with you"? Does it mean, "You aren't a priority to me, but if you want to meet with you, I guess I could fit you in somewhere"? I don't think she meant either of these things, but this is what "sure" sounded like to me. I quickly responded, "Which is it? Yes or no? If you say 'sure,' it sounds like you don't really want to."

My friend struggles with an eating disorder. I had to get her to make her decision clear. Making definite commitments is never easy for someone with an eating disorder. The phrases "I don't know" and "sure" come out of my mouth way too often. And as I sat and listened to my friend try to explain her feelings, I noticed she ended almost every sentence with, "I don't know . . . "

With eating disorders, the desire to please is strong. Not only did I change my appearance for fear of being rejected, but I also had begun to lose my "voice"—the power of my personal opinions—entirely. Disagreeing became dangerous. Voicing my true opinion meant the possibility of rejection. Conformity was a safer option.

At the beginning of my recovery, whenever my counselor asked me how I was doing, I almost always responded, "I don't know." And when Jesse and I got engaged and I began to share deeper parts of myself, it was challenging to share what I was going through.

There's nothing more frustrating than not knowing yourself, your own emotions, likes, and dislikes. But every time I step out and share, I get to know myself better. It's frustrating at times—sometimes I have to sit and think for a while before voicing my thoughts—but I know it's just a part of healing. I must discover who I am and overcome my fear of rejection. It's the only way I'll ever have a voice, the only way I'll ever truly be known by my husband, and the only way we'll truly be able to become one.

Becoming one with my husband does not mean I take on all the things he likes. I used to do this with past boyfriends. I noticed myself liking the music they liked, dressing in styles I thought they'd approve of. When I started dating Jesse, I feared losing my voice again. I feared that I would shut up and be agreeable. He's the last person I'd want to reject me. But I've found that the more I voice my true opinions, even if they're different from his, and even if it means trudging through tedious conversation where we try to figure out what the other person is "really" saying, it's worth it. It's worth knowing if it is me he truly loves.

No man ever really loved me before Jesse. I never let them love me. They may have loved who they thought I was but not who I truly am. Jesse gets to unfold the true me. And I need to know that I am worth pursuing. I want my depths to be discovered. I want to be known, sought out, and delighted in. But I'll never be found if I don't know myself. I'll end up revealing something, but it may not be me. That's not fair to me or him. I don't want to marry a stranger any more than he wants to marry a mannequin.

Only God can tell me who I am. He's the one who made me. Every day I look to Him to define me, to show me what's inside, and to help me get it out. It's been an incredible journey. I'm discovering gifts and passions I never knew I had. I answer questions with "sure" and "I don't know" less frequently. Instead, I've decided to be patient with myself and discover what I really want. My voice is important.

Ask Him

So go ahead. Ask Him. Ask Him who you are. It helps to have a journal and the Bible to search the Scriptures. Wait for His voice. He is always faithful. Know that He only has positive things to say. If you don't feel uplifted or encouraged at what you hear, it's not from Him. Hosea 2:14 says, "Therefore I am now going to allure her; I will lead her into the desert and speak tenderly to her." Trust that when you hear encouraging and tender words in your thoughts, they are from Him, not something you made up. Know that He enjoys you and cannot wait to share His thoughts with you. You are His cherished child. Position your heart to receive. He will show you.

2005

Inspiration: When girls get ready to go out
You Enjoy Myself

Ride excitement, put on paint,
Scold the nerves that cannot wait.
The mirror, the jeans, the stomach stare,
Clear eyes, pull brushes through the hair.
And when I realize where I am
I pause to breathe, run to God's hand.
I'm stressed! Depressed. Encourage me.
Do you love all that You see?
And are You still enthralled by me?
Please help my heart, how can it be?
And so I hide my life in You.
Then all I see is You, shine through.
When You're around, there's no one else.
I smile when You enjoy myself.

CHAPTER 23

O GRACE, RADICAL GRACE

A S I began learning about my identity in Christ, I also began to understand the power of His radical, abundant grace.

I used to think that knowing about grace would give me a license to sin. But the reality is, it's His grace, His kindness that leads us to repentance. Whenever I resorted to bulimia, He never had to tell me that I messed up. All He had to do was say, "I love you," and I was sent running back into His arms.

The Lord is abundant in grace! And when we realize how much He loves us in our mess, it's hard to keep running away. It's just like a forgiving husband with a cheating wife. The wife comes home, and the husband says, with love in his eyes, "I can smell his cologne, and I can see what you're trying to hide, but I want you to know that I love you, and I am for you, and I really, really like who you are. Come here and let me hold you."

If somebody showed me that much love after I had done something so shameful, it would be hard for me to do it again. So why do we keep doing that which we don't want to do? Because we still don't believe 100% that God loves us that much. We think, "Well, He forgave me and loved me that time, but this time He'll have to get mad and abandon me." It's like we're testing Him to see if we can receive His grace and love again. We actually want God to get mad and yell at us or leave us. It would make it much easier to keep sinning. But it's His kindness that leads us to repentance (Romans 2:4).

The following is a journal entry depicting a time when I received His radical grace and came into a greater revelation of His relentless love for me.

March 12, 2006

I'm angry. Really [bleeping] mad. At myself. How ridiculous is this!? I'm angry because there's no excuse, no reason for what I just did. I don't even want to write what I just did. It's wickedness oozing out. Like evil came seeping into my pores, taking over my body, and turning me deranged. And inside, the real me cried. Knowing what I was doing.

God, I pushed against You really hard this time. This time it was hard to do it. I fought against You. I fought so hard to keep Your voice out. But You never left. You kept giving me a way out, but I didn't want to hear it. Why couldn't You just leave!

I had flown home from Washington to my parents' empty house. Two friends picked me up. I should be happy, right? But they left, and I was home alone.

On the flight, I started thinking about what I was gonna eat when I got home and was alone. Classic warning sign of a binge. I caught myself. I turned to You. I closed my eyes and realized how unsatisfying that would be compared to Your presence. I called to You, and You came. I asked You to forgive my foolish thinking . . . thinking that You couldn't satisfy this indescribable need, but a bowl of cereal at home could. Lord, Your presence felt so good in that moment, and I thought about food and didn't want it. My soul was satisfied with the richest of foods.

Now here I am. Miserable. Worn out. Lord, it scares me how rebellious I can be. When I got home and my friends left, I kept stuffing myself, first with nachos when the girls were over, then after they left it was cereal, then peanut butter and jelly rolled in tortillas, then cheese bread, cookies, popcorn, crackers, and cheese. Madly shoving one thing after the other into my mouth. I wanted to get away with it. I didn't want You near. Lord, I pushed and pushed and pushed You out of my mind as I frantically stuffed. I fought hard against Your voice telling me to stop. I was stubborn. Wanting my way.

When I stopped stuffing and began to head upstairs to purge, I got so scared. Outside of Your shelter I felt so afraid and vulnerable. Afraid to lock up the house and turn out the lights. So very alone, like a fawn in an open field full of wolves. I could feel the wolves waiting around every corner, ready to run down the hall and pounce on me, and I couldn't call on You to help. I had to hide so I could purge. So I ran! God, I felt so vulnerable. So alone!

You hold me together. You keep me sane. You give me protection. You satisfy my soul.

Why did it happen? There must be a reason. I'm so frustrated. Let me list some triggers:

1. *I overate this weekend*
2. *Didn't work out therefore believed the lie that I'm fat*
3. *Traveling = change of routine*
4. *Discussing eating disorders with Kate*
5. *Alone at my parents' house*

My eyes burn.
It's 1:30 a.m.
My teeth feel rotten.
I'm a mess without You, God. I fall apart.
I'm mad.
Mad mad mad mad.

Mad because I pushed and fought my way out of Your arms so hard so that I could do it.

Mad because I knew I should stop. Mad because I knew the outcome, but I chose to forget it.

Insanity: doing the same thing over and over again and expecting a different outcome.

I need help.

I can feel the scowl on my face again. It comes on when there's death inside me. A pathetic frown with worried eyes, worried, pensive forehead . . .

I see You, Lord . . . I break . . .

(After writing the last word, I lost it. I saw God's face, and all I could do was cry. I was so humbled. He wasn't mad. He loved me. He held me so tight. And all I could do was cry. I wrote about my experience the next morning. Too worn out to write again that night, I fell asleep, safe in His arms.)

March 13, 2006 (the next morning)

O God. Where can I go from Your mercy? Where can I go from Your love? God, You amaze me as You receive me gladly. There's no fall too great. You conquered it all. Endured everything for me.

Last night when I put down the pen, I lost it. I cried loud like a little baby girl running to her daddy's arms for forgiveness. And Lord, You were right there to say, "Shhshhshh. It's OK. I know. I know. I love you, Jessica. I forgive you, Jessica. It's OK."

My sobs were repulsive, but You held me tighter, stroking my forehead. "It's OK."

How could I, Jesus? How could I! Push You away? Push You away? How could I? After all that You've done! O God, how could I! Why did I? O God, how could I?

You're so good to me. All You've done is be nice to me, come close to me, and set me free. You saved my life...And this is how I repay You? O God. Forgive me. O God. O God. O God. Forgive me.

Even though He forgave me right away, I couldn't stop saying it. Sobbing. Realizing the weight of what I'd done. It ached. But I felt so safe. No longer vulnerable to the enemy's claws, but safe in Daddy's arms. I cried. I was ashamed. But I was forgiven, set free from condemnation.

I nestled close to You. But my back was still to You. I couldn't look at You in the eyes for long. It's so hard for me to receive your radical grace sometimes. I feel so undeserving. Why can't you just be mad? The shame was great. My fall so deliberate. I had fought so hard against You. For momentary gratification. A momentary sense of accomplishment, which is what I feel when I purge, and what's coming up is everything I remember eating. That's so gross. But sin is gross. It's repulsive. Disgusting. Full of death and destruction. No matter how small or great.

Lord. But your grace covers all.

So here I am. I woke up, and now I get a new day. Where can I go from Your mercy, O Lord? Where can I go from Your love? I can't escape

it no matter how hard I try. Your mercy is new every morning. New every
morning. Lord, great is Your love for me. I will be healed. I am healed.

This will be behind me. It is behind me. I am victorious in You!

But I will not forget how Your love covers me, the sorrow, the shame.

I will not forget the immensity of that feeling. The feeling of being cut
off from You. Vulnerable. Getting torn into by the devil's evil little messen-
gers. Scared. Outside of Your protection. Denying Your shelter. And then
returning. Ashamed. O, so ashamed.

O Lord. How can I learn from the way You love me? O Your grace,
radical grace! Your kindness and love lead me to repentance. Your love is
deep. Your love is high. Your love is long. Your love is wide. I cannot compre-
hend it. But o, how I need it! Thank You, Lord. Thank You, Daddy. Thank
You, Father. Dad. Thank You, Daddy. Thank You. Thank You. Thank You.
Thank You.

In this journal entry, you can see how I actually had to resist God's voice to
fight against Him. He kept calling me into His arms, and I deliberately pushed
against Him. It was the most horrible feeling in the world.

Remembering this episode always helped me see how real the enemy's
schemes are—his death threats became very obvious to me in the dark hallways
of my house. It also helped me to know that there is no fall too great. How can
I resist a lover who constantly has His arms extended to me? It's like a little kid
trying to get in trouble by aggravating his mother, trying to get some sort of
reaction so he can receive the punishment he thinks he deserves. But the mother
keeps standing there, with a knowing smile, holding out her arms to embrace
him. Love.

Love will eventually break down the child's pride until he is weeping and
burying his face in his mother's arms.

Eating disorders are a way of giving ourselves the punishment we think we
deserve. But when we experience the immense love of God, we are able to love
ourselves. We can only love with the love we receive from Him—that goes for
loving ourselves, loving others, and loving Him back. If we don't think He loves
us very much, we can't feel love for Him. It's impossible. True love only comes
from Him; and unless we first receive it, we have nothing to give. But when we
get a revelation of His radical grace and receive it into our lives, the natural reac-

tion is to love Him back. Those who have been forgiven much, love much (Luke 7:47).

When I let His love into me—when I receive His grace—it becomes clear to me how much I truly long for Him. I've learned that God is not just a tool to help me get fixed. He's my Daddy, my lover, and my best friend, and I can't stand to be apart from Him. His radical grace keeps me from wanting to run away again.

As you fight, remember how radical His grace is. He doesn't withhold any of it from you. He's not worried about you using it for a license to sin. He knows that when you truly receive His love, you will only be able to react in love. You will be free from the chains that hold you, and you will choose His love over sin every time.

CHAPTER 24

HIS NEARNESS

FURTHER healing came when I received a revelation of the Lord's nearness. I don't need to mess up to come running to Him and feel His nearness. He is always near, always holding out His arms, even in the most mundane moments.

March 14, 2006

Where can I go from Your Spirit? There's nowhere I can turn to escape from Your presence. You're always here.

I come to this revelation again and again. Just a few weeks ago ,I was thinking about God's omnipresence. It's very humbling to think about. I can get weirded out by it, too. Like He's just sitting here, staring at me, madly in love with me. I'm not sure if I like that. There's nothing worse than some guy gawking at you while you eat. It's awkward. Anyway, He's God, not some guy, so I'm sure this picture is a little off. Still, the idea that He's always right here with me confounds me.

I'm overwhelmed by the fact that God is always here. Like right here. I hadn't talked with Him much today, and I stopped dead in my meaningless thoughts and said, "Hey God. You there?" He smiled and said, "Yes. I'm here." The proximity of His voice startled me. He said it like an old friend, knowing, and grinning tenderly at my simple question. He'd been there the whole time, with hardly any recognition from me.

Sometimes I think God's cruising around somewhere else when I'm not talking to Him. I like to think of Him on some mountain peak above the clouds, busy giving breath to the sunset or the next war on wars. A much more appropriate place, I'd say, than hanging out with boring me. Who

wants to hang out with a serious case of self-addiction? Anyway . . . God is
here. He never leaves.
　　And what amazes me most is that I am all He wants.

It's true. He told me in Song of Solomon 7:9. Check it out: "I am my lover's.
I am all He wants. I'm the world to Him!" (The Message). And in chapter 4 verse
9: "You looked at me and I fell in love. One look my way and I was hopelessly
in love!" (The Message).

Then You said:

Walk in the light of My presence, My daughter. Walk in the light of My
presence. I am refining you. That old dead tree, can you see it there? In the
middle of the river? It's nearly completely uprooted. The water is pounding
hard. I am uprooting it because of My spirit, My presence in your life. The
river is powerful, turning into a huge waterfall. At the bottom the mist is
great and marvelous, going everywhere the wind blows. You will go many
places, My daughter. You do not fear being alone. Walk in the light of My
presence. It's not an experience. Not a moment.
　　There was a time when like an eagle you flapped your wings. Pounded
them hard, but didn't get very far. Now I am showing you how to soar. You
will be able to run and jump off cliffs. Opening up your wings, you will soar.
　　You said, Immerse yourself. Don't be afraid to jump in. You'll know when
it's time to move on, but for now, jump in! Become submerged! Immerse
yourself in the light of My presence. You'll know when to be loud and when
to be peaceful. Like an eagle. Bold, but with the gentleness of a dove.

He is always speaking. He is always adoring. His love is constant. It never
changes. What might change is your ability to receive His love, to recognize His
nearness, to realize His pleasure over you. His love won't get bigger when you get
better. He loves you with the same intense love that He will love you with when
you're living the future you envision. He loves you the same even through your
deepest pits. He loves you the same whether you've ignored Him or spent hours
with Him. His nearness cannot be earned.

Knowing His unconditional love lifts us right out of any pit we might be found in. It causes us to move, to take action, to be who we were created to be, full of life and joy.

And so here I am writing.
And here I am healing.
I am learning to live not from a place of shame but from a place of victory and the nearness of my King.

CHAPTER 25

THE DRESSING ROOM

WHILE God's truth was breaking through, certain situations still stirred up old thoughts. Shopping was one of them. Trying on clothes and looking in the mirror brought up familiar spirits—thoughts I had lived with for so long that I almost enjoyed them. Like self-pity and self-hatred. They often felt like old friends. I had to take these thoughts captive. Otherwise, the enemy's ways, which are destructive, would continue to manifest in my life.

December 2006

Bathing Suits

O, bathing suits. I used to wear them all the time. I used to live in them. O God, help me . . . bathing suits. It's easier to not think about my body in the winter when I'm covered. Big zip-up sweatshirts work wonders. But it's winter, and we're going to Hawaii. Hawaii! I should be excited, but I'm scared. I don't want to be seen. Especially by my own family, who will probably be surprised at how I've changed. "They're gonna be disappointed, my brother's gonna be embarrassed, people are gonna stare, Mom's gonna ask about how 'things' are going."

But how do I know that? Why do I make this stuff up and think that it's fact? Man, those lies keep replaying like bad Old Navy commercials. I can see it all. The beach, the people, their eyes—they're focused not on my face but on all the parts I'm self-conscious about. The parts that aren't smooth anymore. I know, I'll just swim in my clothes. Good Lord, I never thought I'd want to do that. Sick. I'm becoming a tourist! I used to be cool. Or maybe I'll just never

147

go down to the water. Yeah, right. I know I can't stay away from the ocean. I'll go crazy. Man, why should I put myself in this cage? It sucks!

I Choose Life

I'm gonna do something about it. . . . Jessica, it's OK.

I have a choice here. I can choose to sit and sulk, to analyze, to live in fear of what people think. But you know what? I'm sick of letting strangers have control over me. I'm sick of giving them power. I want to be like the grandma who's playing paddleball with her grandson in her bathing suit on the beach. She's beautiful. She's confident in her body. And I don't see fat. Just how beautiful she is and how much fun she looks as if she's having. How free she is. And I want that.

It's like just the other day I was thinking about what attracted me to certain guys. (I wrote this before meeting my husband.) It's never the body. It's always the spirit. I can see a guy with an imperfect body who's very attractive because he's not full of himself, not self-conscious, but confident, alive, and present. Man, I really need to enjoy life more.

Today I have the opportunity to choose. (Reading this sentence requires that you download India.Arie's "I Choose" and rock out.) I can choose to lose life to self-hatred and self-pity. Or I can choose to be the best that I can be. To realize that my body does not dictate who I am. To put on that suit and say, "Hello, world!" This is me! And the only way they'll see me is if I'm not focused on me. If I'm self-conscious, they'll see my body. If I'm confident, they'll see my spirit and the Spirit living inside me.

Bringing My Fear into the Light

I brought up my fear to my mom that week. It was a huge breakthrough to be able to share my fears with her. Smiling, I said in a playful, kind of joking but deep down really serious tone, "Hey, so, let's go to the mountains instead."

She looked at me with those *now*-you-tell-me eyes and said, "Honey, we're already going to Hawaii. The trip's all booked. Now you want to go skiing? I thought you didn't like the cold."

It's true. I don't. My fingers and toes lose circulation due to Reynaud's disease. That's why God birthed me in Southern California. I gave her one of those whiney smiles, like when a child gets caught doing something wrong, and said, "I know. I'm just kidding, but I just . . . I don't want to be in a bathing suit."

My mother put down the mail, looked straight into my eyes, and said, "Honey, you have no need to worry."

"But you don't understand! I . . . "

"Honey, listen to me. You are beautiful. You think guys care about how you look?"

"Yeah. Of course."

"That's not what turns guys on."

"Well, then, how come that's all guys ever talk about?"

"Honey, you listen to me. Men are not turned on by perfect bodies." (I'm picturing heads turning as a hot woman walks by and thinking, "Yeah, right.") She saw my thought and said, "They're not. Trust me. I'm married. Men have one button, and any woman can push it. Why do you think all women of all shapes and sizes are married?"

Now don't get me wrong, the issue is not whether or not someone will marry us. We must learn that it's not about men. The fear of man brings a snare, but perfect love casts out all fear. Falling madly in love with Jesus, the perfect lover, eliminates that annoying longing to turn heads. It must be about Him first and foremost. It must be about knowing Him as your husband. No man can define you.

I remembered something a friend once told me. I was confessing to her about how marriage had been on my mind. How ironic that as soon as I felt ready for marriage, my body was not looking the way I wanted it to. She told me, "Jessica, the man of your dreams is gonna fall in love with you. Do you want a guy who's gonna fall in love with you because you've slaved away at the gym and been on a no-carb diet? No, because if that's why he falls in love with you, then the rest of your marriage you'll be living in fear. You'll be trapped trying to maintain that body, fearful that if it changes he'll fall out of love. You don't want that. You want a man who loves *you*. Not your body. And when he loves you, he'll love your body, too.

"Trust me," she continued. "My husband tells me all the time how much he loves my body, and the funny thing is, he loves the parts I hate the most. I mean, Jessica, he loves my love handles!" We both chuckled. "Really! He told me never to lose them. I jokingly said, 'What if I go to the gym and work them off?' He got kind of upset and all serious on me and said, 'No! I'm serious. I love them.

I'm not just saying that. Do not lose them. They're softness and feminineness and beautiful, and I just wanna grab 'em!'"

We both laughed, and I felt hope welling up inside of me. I felt beautiful.

The Miracle in the Dressing Room

Bathing suits, bathing suits, bathing suits . . . I had to get a new one. In the few short months between summer and winter, I had managed to outgrow my old ones. And there I was faced with another choice. I could look at the situation and see it as a failure. As something I should be ashamed of. Or I could look at is as a victory. Victory over bulimia! I had gone without purging for three whole months! Man, that was a huge victory. And I decided that it was OK if the pendulum swung to the opposite of anorexia. I knew that eventually, it would even out, and I would learn how to eat normally, if there is any such thing as normally. Intuitively is a better word.

Bathing suits. Now, Target would never be my first choice for bathing suit shopping. Such an endeavor would be highly frowned upon by the Newport Beach culture. However, I knew they sold suits that had adequate butt coverage. You know, the kind where you can actually distinguish between the front and the back.

So I made up my mind not to get mad at my image in the mirror and grabbed a few of the suits with ample butts. In the past, size was always a huge deal. Numbers on scales, numbers on clothes, it all mattered. It all held power over my mood. I got so frustrated when the clothes never looked like they did on the mannequin. It made me feel as if there was something wrong with me. Trying on twenty pairs of jeans can be very depressing. And bathing suits were even worse.

Inside the dressing room, I thought, *OK, here we go. Don't analyze. Just put it on, see if it fits. If it does, great; if not, that's all it means—it doesn't fit. It doesn't mean you're fat, or ugly, or abnormal, or that you need to decide to go on another diet, or that if you were skinnier life would be easier. It just means it doesn't fit, and that's OK. I've got to live my life, and I don't want it to revolve around whether or not I fit into a tiny bathing suit.*

So I did it! I picked out two suits. I didn't stare forever, just made sure they fit, accepted the way my body looked, and moved on. And people say miracles never happen. Well, I'm here to tell you that a miracle happened that day in the dressing room. God granted me the grace to accept the things I cannot change—to be OK with the body that God gave me to live inside of.

Accepting My Body

It takes a lot of rewiring to get to the point of loving and accepting something that everything and everyone around you tells you is wrong. Every day, messages pour in, telling us that our bodies should always be diligently and aggressively attacked, reduced, slimmed, and chiseled. You should be embarrassed if it's not.

As I mentioned in the beginning, the media spends billions of dollars every year to make us feel miserable about the way we look. Just the other day, I received an email for a free trial tube of cellulite cream. Oooh! Cellulite cream! I briefly thought about ordering it, figuring I could retrieve the package from the mail before my roommates found it. But then I caught myself and realized I had been deceived. The master deceiver was hard at work, staring me in the face with a free offer of cellulite cream. He might as well have just come on in for tea and said politely, while delicately swirling his chai, "Jessica, cellulite is ugly and disgusting, and you have it. It is not something someone your age should have. You need to get rid of it in order to be beautiful. If you don't, people will be grossed out by you. What man could ever love you? You're going to need a lot of cream. It can't hurt to try. It's free, for goodness' sake. What are you going to lose?"

Sick! He's so slimy. If so many people have cellulite, why is it ugly? Whoever decided it was ugly in the first place? The tabloids have a ball with photos of stars in their suits: "Even Nicole Richie Has Cellulite!" The poor thing already looks like a skeleton. Now even that's not enough. Nothing's ever enough.

And it's no different with us, except of course we're usually not *Cosmopolitan's* next cover girl. We really need to stop letting the world tell us how to look. It sucks the life out of us. We can have cellulite no matter how thin we are. Most times it's something we genetically inherit, like eye color—nothing to be ashamed of.

So I went to Hawaii. It was hard. I had to focus on being me instead of comparing myself to everyone, instead of fearing that my brother was embarrassed by me. I had to keep the focus on my family, on loving them, on getting to know them, on laughing, on being free. I'm still not where I want to be as far as freedom is concerned, but I'm making progress, and that's what it's all about.

CHAPTER 26

STAYING OPEN

I N addition to not letting size dictate my emotions, I also learned important lessons not just about being open but also about staying open. Proverbs 17:19 says, "She who builds a high gate invites destruction." No matter how long I've been in recovery, I have to continue to bring my inner battle into the light. Isolation always leads to destruction. Here is an incident I wrote about while visiting a friend in Oregon.

January 3, 2007

> *Here I am in Oregon, and something happened that I must write down. I probably would not be writing now had I kept my mouth shut, barred with lock and key. I tend to do that. Resort to silence.*
>
> *Silence. It's one of comparison's jobs: to tighten stubborn lips and stir the thick paste of negative emotions—to bring resentment, depression, and bitterness to the surface. We women do this often. But today I decided to share my battle with a friend.*
>
> *This morning I went to the gym with Sarah. I was not excited. My feet dragged heavily as the sound of impending treadmills and Precor machines groaned. Bum bum. Bum bum. Bum bum.*
>
> *Trying to avoid the intense glances of sweaty bodies, I walked the Green Mile to my machine. "The guy behind you is looking at your butt," the lies said, "and it's not a pretty sight. There's probably lint on it." I did a quick cheek check with my hand and resumed focus. Burn calories.*
>
> *O great. Look at all those TVs. There were about ten TVs in my view, half of which were teleprompting advice about diet, even on The 700 Club. Eat this much of this type of food X amount of time before working out . . .*

(Dang it. I already messed that one up) . . . and eat this much of that type of food Y amount of time following a workout so that the (insert impressive scientific noun) in your muscles will (insert impressive scientific verb) in this really cool way, and you'll lose weight. And of course there's the never-ending stream of commercials with scary-skinny women remarking in a way-too-fast voice how TurboTrim is the fastest weight-loss supplement on the market.

Man, I totally got sucked in. My rational mind knew all that stuff was crap, but it still got to my emotions. I started thinking about how "fat" I was and how I should change the way I ate. The liar was loud: "I should be a good steward of my body, so I should eat like 'they' say I should so I'll be skinny, and then I'll be happy."

Interrupting my spiraling thoughts, Sarah moved back a few rows to a treadmill. I followed suit hoping a change would help silence the liar and stave off the reluctance to work out. I chose a Stairmaster behind her. Off I went at a not-so-intense pace while Sarah was running the ten-meter dash. "She's gonna burn more calories than you," the liar said. "That's OK; I'll just eat less at lunch." Now the liar tricked me into believing that second voice was mine, but it was still his, rationalizing how I could still come out on top. "My workout's a fat-burning one, and hers is cardio," I justified, unaware that my justifications were also competitive and unhealthy.

My time on the stairs was up, and she was still going. "Maybe if I move to the machine next to her, she'll get the clue that I'm done, and she'll stop too. She cannot work out more than I do. She already looks better than me. Don't let her work out more." I cranked up the treadmill next to her to a fast pace. Miserable, I asked, "How much longer you gonna go for?"

"Another five, and then a five-minute cool down," she replied, unaware of the battle going on inside my head.

"No," I moaned, again hoping this would stop her.

"You can stop if you want, I'm just gonna finish up here."

"But you don't understand," the voice that only I could hear continued, "I have to work out as much as you." Inside I sulked. I kept picturing my naked body, my body from the back in a bathing suit, the image that got stuck when I obsessed a few weeks ago.

Remember that little miracle that happened in the Target dressing room? Well, that night as my new bathing suits lay there in my room, they started talking to me: "You should try us on again. I don't think you got a good enough look. You might even look better in this lighting." So on went a suit. I approached the mirror and turned, grabbing a hand-held to get a good look at the back. "Uhh!" I gasped. "I can't look like that! That's how I look? O my gosh! O my gosh!" I pulled here and pushed there, turning from side to side and feeling more and more infuriated at myself by the second. I tried to tell myself it was OK, but it was too late. The images were stuck.

I quietly cried myself to sleep that night.

Those were the images I was picturing in the gym. And as I saw them, fat man Depression collapsed from his standing position to a lazy sprawl atop my emotions, squashing poor Joy as she tried to skip out of the way. I picked up the pace again, "Run! You need it," the voice said. "But I don't want to! I'm tired. I have a cold." My body was saying, "Rest." As I stepped off the machine, Bitterness began taking swings at Depression lying there.

Mad tears welled because Sarah was still running. I looked for a place to stretch but still could not bear the thought of sitting down while she was burning away, so I went to the opposite end of the long line of treadmills, cranked up the incline, and walked, determined to shut the voice up. I turned on worship music, fought the tears, and fought the greeter at the door to the pity party.

Jesus, help me focus on You. What's going on? Why do I feel like this? I don't want to be bitter at Sarah. I started mouthing the words and felt better that I couldn't see what Sarah was doing. She finished, and we moved on downstairs. Her joy embittered me even more. And the whole time, God was impressing on my spirit that I needed to open my mouth and share what was going on inside my head, but I didn't want to. Pride wouldn't let me. The last thing I wanted to do was share my feelings. Way too mushy and vulnerable.

So I keep silent.

Suck Up Your Pride and Share

Back at the apartment, I crumpled to the floor and stared at the ceiling.

"Why are you so sleepy?" Sarah asked.

"I dunno."

"Now's your chance," Wisdom said. "Tell her now! Tell her how you're feeling."

After tiptoeing around possibilities of why I could be tired, I finally said, "I had a really difficult experience at the gym just now."

"O, really? What happened?"

I was surprised at the shock in her voice. I thought I was being obvious. I told her what happened, grudgingly confessing my comparison and competition with her. She listened and began getting extremely mad at the devil for beating me up like that. She even confessed to me how she finds herself wanting to be more like me at times.

We decided to declare the truth together, and the color started coming back into my cheeks. I finally leaped off the ground and hit the shower. It was all over. The lies were silenced. I felt loved. I felt connected. And all I had to do was open my mouth.

Finds Friends to Confide In

I want to get better at opening my mouth sooner. Even if this means I have to do it every hour. Pride often keeps me from opening my mouth. I think I'll be an annoying and irrational burden. But the friends I do confide in, I can trust. I know they're not going say, "It's OK; we all have hard times like that." That would make me feel as if they really don't understand.

I know my friends and husband will listen and get mad at the devil with me. I know that they won't use flattery to help. "O, Jessica, you're not fat. You're beautiful. Stop whining." That's not what I need to hear. I need to know that they recognize how intense the battle can be for me. I need to know that they will always be there to disagree with the enemy's lies and stand by my side. I need to know they don't think I'm just looking for attention. But I also need help remembering that I'm beautiful.

Find at least one friend you can confide in. Let her know you need her help. Call her more than you think you need to. Never think you can let it slide. The sooner you get the thoughts out into the open, the sooner they will stop. Once the enemy is exposed, he has no strength.

It's easy to think, *It's no big deal. I can fight this on my own.* But that's pride. Eating disorders force you to live a walled-off, independent life. Asking for help is the last thing you'll want to do. It's scary to feel as if you're losing control. It's foreign, and you don't know what the outcome will be. It feels easier to resort to hiding, because at least you know the outcome, even if it's negative.

You must choose to face your fear and reach out, because by sharing and being humble, you're gaining control and not losing it. Your friends will help you see reality. Make a decision to keep your connections open, no matter how long you've been fighting. Overcoming your fear is well worth it.

CHAPTER 27

EATING HABITS, UP FOR GRABS!

BECAUSE eating disorders can make eating very confusing, I have often adopted other people's eating habits. If we were out to dinner, I would look around to see how fast people were eating or how much was left on their plates so I would know how much I should leave on mine to feel normal or to come out on top. This was especially true as I began branching out and trying new foods.

I remember an instance in February of 2007 when some of my guy friends invited a bunch of us girls over for a home-cooked Valentine's Day meal. They served pasta, something I never ate. But I had come a long way in incorporating "off-limits" foods into my diet. Besides, I hated it when people asked why I wasn't eating certain things. I hated to be high maintenance. I also hated people thinking I only ate healthy food like salad. If they only knew.

Because pasta was something I always avoided, I found myself looking at other people's plates in order to judge how I should eat it. My roommate finished her plate, and she's not a big eater. She's also very petite. She eats when she's hungry. I judged that I too could finish my plate without being a pig. I left that night uncomfortably full.

All night I battled the voices of "I'm fat," and "You shouldn't have eaten that," and "That's what happens when you eat bad foods like pasta. Now you've really blown it. You could purge and fix your mistake." Luckily I fought and won that battle, but I could have avoided it altogether.

The problem is, I am not Lily or Dan or Kim or La Donna or Ellen. I am Jessica, and I need to start eating for me—to listen to those wonderful cues God placed inside my body so that I don't cause it harm. Learning to eat intuitively helped me to separate biological signals of hunger from emotional signals. I learned to slow down and stop eating when the food stopped tasting good instead of mindlessly eating cookie after cookie. The first one tasted the best anyway.

I'm sure you can attest to this. Even a large apple stops satisfying by the time you get down to the last few bites. Discover what your body actually wants by slowing things down. Believe that you have a right to enjoy food, but that you don't have to finish everything on your plate.

I once heard God tell me, "The more you feed it [your body], the more alive it becomes." This was not a message to starve myself. I knew God meant that when I stuff myself to feed an unmet emotional desire, my body becomes my focus. When I fed the sin of using food as comfort instead of God, I became enslaved again. I felt my body more. It, and the feeling of fullness, became my focus instead of friends and others around me.

As God continues to set me free, dinners out become more about the people, about being present, open and real, and less about the food. Sometimes the liar tries to trick me into getting the sandwich so I won't always be the salad girl, but when I realize what I really want, I'm able to order for *me*, not for the liar and not for the approval of others. I can order the sandwich or the salad or the tacos. And I don't have to count calories. My body knows how much it needs, and I'm finally learning to listen.

Still Restricting

Not only has eating out with others been something I've needed to surrender to God, but I have also had to surrender my daily eating routine. One day I was meeting with one of my friends from a counseling group when she asked, "Are you still restricting?" She waited for my response as I considered her question, and then she continued, "I mean, what are you rewarding yourself for?"

I had shared with our little support group that night how I'd had another bad weekend with eating too much. I hadn't purged in months, but my problem then was that I still overate periodically to fill a void.

My friend's question was prompted because I shared how I was rewarding myself over the weekend for having a good week. The "reward" had turned into a weekend-long, over-eating spree. As I thought about her question, I realized that I did still have my rules during the week and was therefore still restricting. I tried to eat healthy Monday through Friday, which meant no dessert. I even employed my no-eating-past-X p.m. rule.

I looked forward to the weekends, because I always allowed myself to get a treat. But the weekend started Friday or even Thursday. The treat turned into grabbing any sweets available at a birthday party or baby shower or bridal shower or church hospitality table. I tricked myself into thinking I owed it to myself for being so good all week. But by Sunday night, I felt disgusting.

Finally I replied, "I guess I am still restricting. I had no idea. I thought I was just trying to be healthy." I finally realized what the problem had been. The rules were still there, keeping me in control. When I let go of the rules for the weekend, I didn't know how to listen to my body's cues. I just went into famine mode and hoarded all the sweets I came in contact with.

I told the group that week that I would let go of the rules and even start incorporating small desserts with my dinner if I wanted. At first, I was afraid to keep anything sweet in the freezer. I bought packaged ice cream sandwiches from Trader Joe's because I didn't want a tub of anything that might trigger portion-control anxiety.

And to my surprise, I didn't get out of control. I had a piece of pizza for lunch that Tuesday without overanalyzing it. (Pizza! I know!) I had an ice cream sandwich after dinner on Wednesday and didn't want more or even feel guilty about it. I realized that hanging out with my friend, who wanted the free pizza, was more important than finding a salad, and that having an ice cream on a Wednesday didn't mean my week was ruined.

Because I stopped restricting, I found myself craving sweets less often. It was amazing to feel that the eating disorder wasn't in charge anymore.

In your recovery, what rules are you still holding onto that may be keeping you from going to the next level? Many times we do things that we think are perfectly healthy but are really keeping us in the enemy's stronghold.

I had been living with the weekend rule for a long time because I had heard someone's Weight Watchers testimony on TV. The woman told of how her Sunday slice of cheesecake kept her sane. Also, my mom ate healthy during the week and rewarded herself with a Ruby Burger at Ruby's Diner on Sundays after church. That might be fine for her but not for someone who has been severely bound by eating disorders for years.

What influences in your life have led you to believe that what you are doing is healthy for you? Often the people who influence us have unhealthy relationships with food as well. Changing eating habits must be paired with leaning on Jesus. Remember, it's not just about fixing a mentality. It's about building a relationship. It's about letting the Author of Peace calm your nerves and wash over you with His love. When you are confident in who you are as His child, your anxiety over food will fall away.

CHAPTER 28

CONNECTING AND BEING SPONTANEOUS

WORKING full-time as a campus missionary at the University of San Diego provided many opportunities for me to grow.

One day in 2007, a girl I was mentoring invited me to a last-minute dinner at the Caff (the cafeteria at the University of San Diego). I said OK and was excited to meet her and her friends later that night. It shocked me that I was agreeing to come. I had to stop and make sure I wasn't dreaming. I had to make sure I wasn't making a mistake. The decision came too easily.

You see, the *me* before the freedom would have freaked out and declined. A barrage of thoughts would have entered my mind: *Do they have anything I can eat? How many hours will it have been between then and the last time I ate? 5:30? I can't eat then. If I eat then, it'll mess up my metabolism. I have to stay on schedule. I probably won't even be hungry then. Besides, I hate people watching me eat. . . .* "No. I can't go. But thanks." And that would have been it.

Instead, I was able to enjoy the friendship of two amazing young women and share pieces of myself with them. I was surprised that I wasn't thinking about the food except when I realized that I wasn't thinking about the food. I was engaged. I was present. I was free.

The *me* before the freedom would have missed out on an opportunity to bond. I would have missed the chance to rub shoulders with students, which is an obviously important aspect of campus ministry. I can't love if I stay isolated. Isolation means I only care about me. Last time I checked, friendships involve more people than me.

I'm glad I don't have to freak out over dinner offers anymore. I never thought

I could have so much fun in my old school cafeteria, a place that used to graciously facilitate my eating disorder.

That night, we animatedly swapped stories of God's goodness and left feeling more satisfied than any meal could ever make me feel.

Connecting with Him and Others

We need each other. As we learn to press into our relationship with God, we free ourselves to be present, to connect, to have the friendships we truly desire.

The first step in connecting is keeping your conscience clear before God and others. When it's clear, you have nothing to hide, and you can truly be present and engaged with people. So many times at social events, the anxiety led me to hover around the snack table. Eating became a substitute for intimacy. I would be chatting with someone but hiding my true self between mouthfuls, trying to avoid the awkward feelings of forced conversation. I also found myself focusing on what other people were eating. I was either staying "in control" while judging others for eating so much, or I was mindlessly eating, trying to gain a sense of peace amidst the storm in my mind. The food was the focus.

I was able to connect with others that night in the school cafeteria because I wasn't ruled by selfishness and fear anymore. I was ruled by my desire for intimacy with God and His children, my brothers and sisters. I knew that I had something to give and something to receive.

Connecting with others is not only a sign of healing, it's also necessary for healing. Our world is dying for lack of intimacy. It needs a deep healing that only His heart and people of His heart can give.

The Father has put into each one of us the keys to this world's healing: He has given us His Spirit and the authority to operate from His kingdom. If we know Jesus, the same Spirit—not some weaker version—the *same* Spirit that raised Jesus from the dead lives inside us. If we listen to His heart, He will lead us into compassion for others. We will connect. We will bring His kingdom to earth.

Jesus took pleasure in connecting with others. He saw people, and He saw the Father and the Father's heart; and out of that intimacy, a power was released that opened blind eyes and restored twisted limbs. We must abide in the intimacy of the Father. It is our key to healing.

CHAPTER 29

SOME DAYS ARE HARDER THAN OTHERS

IN healing, I've learned that no matter how free I am, it doesn't mean the enemy won't try to pull me back into old thoughts.

In 2008, I was in a coffee shop in San Diego. Summer was in full bloom, and the girls were wearing skimpier clothes. And as I was sitting there, it seemed that every girl that walked into the coffee shop was perfectly put together. Perfect bodies. Trendy outfits.

Funny—when I left the house that morning, my jeans and T-shirt looked good on me. I was even having a good hair day. Now I needed a new wardrobe and new hairstyle, and I seriously needed to stop eating so much. I was suddenly boring, unattractive, and bland. It didn't matter that I was engaged to a wonderful man who always called me beautiful. Suddenly these girls were a threat, something for my fiancé's eyes to catch. And in that moment, telling myself I was beautiful wasn't enough. Everything around me was telling me I wasn't measuring up. I felt caught off guard and overwhelmed with sudden panic and the "realization" that I wasn't beautiful.

It wasn't until I remembered that the enemy hates me and wants me to feel this way that I came to my senses. The women around me were no longer a threat; they were God's precious daughters, probably daughters in desperate need of a loving Father.

When the enemy's schemes come to light, it's easier to take our eyes off ourselves and focus on the spiritual battle at hand. We become aware of the arms of our loving Father who wants to be our refuge. His hugs make it so much easier to see the need in others, not in judgment, but in compassion.

That day in the coffee shop, I was a little worried about how easily I had suddenly slipped into this state of depression and feelings of worthlessness. I thought I was healed. But then I remembered that just because I think certain thoughts, doesn't mean I'm still messed up. These thoughts are not coming from my spirit. The thoughts are not a part of me anymore. Instead, they are coming from the outside.

Just as when the devil left Jesus for a more "opportune time," some days are going be harder than others. It doesn't mean I'm still messed up. It just means the enemy still hates me and is threatened by my freedom. And that's OK, because "He who is in me is greater than he who is in the world" (1 John 4:4). As long as I know that, I can keep myself from believing that I'm still trapped. I am free, and bondage is not in my nature anymore. The thoughts aren't of me, they're of the evil one; and I don't have to agree with him.

CHAPTER 30

IS THERE REALLY A WAY OUT?

IS there really a way out? Often I've thought this. Here's the trap: If I'm free from eating rules, I'll get fat. If I'm fat, I can't feel free because I am wrapped in insecurity about my weight and am therefore self-focused. Can I have freedom and still have a good body? That seemed impossible.

I have had many times of frustration over this issue. Many times I've felt free when actually food was still a huge focus, causing me to gain more weight. Other times I've felt free, when I actually still had several rules keeping me thin. Food was still creating the emotions of fear, anxiety, bondage, and shame. This is not freedom. So is there really a way out?

The answer is yes. When I'm truly free, I listen to my body more. It's pretty smart, and I'm learning to trust it. Am I constantly craving something sweet? Maybe I need to incorporate more grains into my diet. I found when I started incorporating healthy carbs into my diet, I craved sweets less. I spent less time thinking about food.

I remember how I used to be so jealous that my roommate could buy ice cream and have it in the freezer for months, usually forgetting that it was there, and sometimes remembering and having a small bowl. How could she do that? I knew more about what food she had in the fridge and pantry than she did. I was so jealous of her freedom.

I can proudly say that Jesse and I have had a bag of chocolates in the freezer for a few months now. I forget that they're even there. Sometimes I really crave chocolate and have a piece. But I'm not ashamed, and I don't finish the whole bag.

Of course, there is wisdom in not keeping certain things in the house. I don't buy what may be a trigger for me. Our home group Bible study left two boxes of cookies at the house one night. I wasn't feeling strong and asked Jesse to get rid of them, even though it's still hard for me to throw food away. And that's perfectly OK with me. I just need to be honest with myself and with him. He understands and is very supportive. He doesn't necessarily want them around either, for his own sake.

The freedom comes when life does not revolve around my body. When I'm not obsessed with food, I eat when I'm hungry and am wise about deciding when to have dessert. I eat based on what my body needs and wants, and not on rules and not on how much or little others are eating.

Freedom comes when I quit placing my hope on losing weight or gaining comfort from food. For example, as I wrote this book, there were times when my perfectionist tendencies created anxiety. I sometimes pictured myself the following day, writing in a coffee shop and snacking on a cookie or muffin. The image always looked so comforting, as if all of my anxieties would be calmed when I got alone and was finally able to get that cozy treat in the privacy of my own world. I have to realize that in those moments, I'm putting my hope in food!

Instead, I decide to say, "Food will never satisfy my desires, but God, You will. Will You come and bring me comfort? Will You come into my hurting places right now? I know Your comfort and healing is much better than food. Come and show me what I am truly longing for." And almost every time I do this, the lies are silenced. His comfort comes in, and my heart is satisfied.

Because we need to eat every day, sometimes it's hard to know if it's "OK" to eat. Am I eating for me or the disorder? How do I know when I'm resorting to old patterns? The answer is: when I want to be alone to do it. If I'm waiting for Jesse to leave so I can get that treat, I know I'm not eating in freedom. I'm doing it in fear. Remember this trick when you're not sure if you're eating emotionally or just eating. Ask yourself, "Am I hiding to eat or eating to hide? Am I ashamed?" If either of these things is true, you are not acting in freedom.

Being free does not mean eat, eat, eat anything I want, whenever I want. In that scenario, food is still the dominant thought in my head. Being free means that food is no longer a focus in my life. Suddenly, other people become more important. My eyes don't see myself or my body or others' bodies with the same eyes anymore. They see God. They see others' spirits. Instead of depression, I feel compassion and love toward others. Instead of boredom, I feel the joy of His presence. Instead of worthlessness, I feel His approval and liberating love. I know that who I am is the one God wants to spend time with. Not because I did anything special, but because I'm His daughter. I am present. I am free.

CHAPTER 31

THINK LOVELY THOUGHTS

IN healing, there were many transformations my mind had to go through. This included thinking positive thoughts. I was accustomed to perfectionism's persistent abuse. She told me what was wrong with me and what needed to be fixed. I often thought, My life would be better if . . . Instead, I had to train my mind to notice the good. I had to realize that while I will always be in a process of growing, I am also already complete in Him. The following are a few exercises I did while in counseling that helped me renew my mind and think positive thoughts.

Write a List of What You Are Thankful For

I made a list of things I was thankful for. It started with simple things like: I'm thankful for my family, for the roof over my head, that I can afford to live in San Diego; and it evolved into things I liked about myself: I'm thankful that I am artistic, that I can play the piano, that I have a healthy body, lungs and legs that can take me on runs. I kept writing until I got tired. I'd had no idea how many things I had to be thankful for. I just needed the right perspective.

The enemy loves putting blinders on us so we can't see. If you held a penny in front of your eye, you wouldn't be able to see much else, even though a penny is small. Our problems and flaws can be the same way when we hold them close.

Instead, start focusing on the good in your life. Make a list of things you are thankful for and things you like about yourself. Much like the lesson on lightening up, this will help free you up to embrace how amazing you really are. It will dig you out of depression and self-pity and help spring-load you into joy and heavenly-mindedness.

I found that giving thanks always led me into His presence. Psalm 100:4

says, "Enter his gates with thanksgiving and his courts with praise; give thanks to him and praise his name." In other words, enter with the password "Thank You." There's no joy without rejoicing. You have a choice in being joyful. Simply start thanking Him, and you'll find that smile you've been missing.

One time at home group, we asked everyone in the group to rate their joy level on a scale of one to ten. One of the girls said she was at about a four. So we told her, "Well, there's no joy without rejoicing. Get up and start shouting, 'Thank You, Jesus!'"

She looked at us with an expression that said, "This is lame. Are you serious?"

"Get up!" we said to encourage her.

She finally did and started saying "Thank You" in passionless tones.

"Believe it!" We encouraged again.

Knowing we wouldn't give up, she exaggerated her "joy" by jumping up and down, clapping, and shouting, "Thank You, Jesuuuuus! Thank You, thank You, thank You!" What started as forced exclamations soon became true outbursts of gratitude. She was finally smiling.

"How are you doing now?"

With a huge grin, she replied, "I'm at an eight."

You might be thinking, This is the cheesiest thing I've ever heard. But trust me - I'm not talking about paste-on-a-smile-religion here. I'm talking about the power of the Living King. His joy is truly available to us if we would just suck up our pride, and our skepticism—we've all been jaded by hypocrisy—and reach out to His promises.

What looks silly and foolish is power to those who believe. For "God was pleased through the foolishness of what was preached to save those who believe" (1 Corinthians 1:21). He chose the foolish things of the world to confound those who are wise in their own eyes.

If we look at Proverbs 8, we get a clear picture of what true wisdom is. Not only do kings reign by wisdom, but verse 30 says, "Then (before the world began) I (wisdom) was the craftsman at his side. I was filled with delight day after day, rejoicing always in his presence" (parenthesis mine).

True wisdom rejoices. No matter how you feel, start thanking God. Let your heart be overwhelmed by His goodness. In doing so, you allow Him to be the Giver of Joy in your life. Soon you'll start to recognize the ways in which He is always moving on your behalf.

"The cheerful heart has a continual feast" (Proverbs 15:15).

What Is Beauty?

In group therapy we were told to write out our definitions of beauty, both from the eating-disorder's perspective and the truth of God. This was a revealing exercise for me. I had no idea how far my definition of beauty had strayed from the truth.

My previous definition of beauty:

Skinny. Waiflike skinny. Skinny so that anything you put on looks good. Skinny. Skinny to the point that there's only muscle, bone, and skin, no fat. It's a size X. It's XXX pounds or less. Beauty is skinny, toned and tan. It's straight hair, smooth skin. It's no blemishes. It's white teeth. Straight teeth. It's clear eyes and a flat stomach. With definition. Beauty is looking down and not seeing a bulge. It's looking in the mirror from all angles, all positions: sitting, standing, lying down. It's looking and moving around and seeing everything looking smooth and strong with no bulging fat. It's having bones stick out in only the right places: the collarbone, ribs, hips, wrists, knees, ankles, shoulders, slight definition on the chest bone. Beauty is a defined jaw bone, high cheeks, even eyes. It's symmetry. It comes from spending hours at the gym or going on runs. It comes from eating no carbs. It's what happens when your calorie output is far greater than your calorie input. It's perfect outfits. It's turning heads. Some people are naturally beautiful, but for most, beauty is a product of discipline.

My current definition of beauty (2006):

Beauty is being alive on the inside. It's when you're so in love with God, so intimately close to Him, so obedient to His will, that your entire being shines. Your eyes glow and radiate His love. There's so much of His life inside that it pours out of you, and you can't help but smile and love and feel loved. It's knowing who you are in Him. It's feeling His security. It's knowing that who you are has nothing to do with your body. It's when you forget about yourself and become love. Beauty is when your new self has been renewed in the knowledge and image of its Creator. It's letting people see Jesus. It's standing in God's presence so much that your face reflects His. It's looking deeper into your eyes, past the color, and seeing yourself and the Holy Spirit there together. Members of one body. It's a heart at rest, anxiety- and worry-free. It's being comfortable in your own skin. Beauty is a quality of the heart that has come alive and is expressing itself on the outside. It's noticing others hearts and not being distracted by your own body. It's catching glimpses in the mirror and seeing smiling eyes of pure gratitude and joy shining back. And I want that kind of beauty.

Writing out your definitions will help you put things into perspective. It'll help you step back and take a look at what beauty really is.

Writing Wrongs

Our group counselor also had us do an exercise called "Writing Wrongs." We wrote letters of apology to our bodies for treating them the way we had. This helped me be thankful for my body and actually feel compassion for it. I reversed the negative words by speaking life over my body. Here's what I wrote:

November 20, 2006

Dear Body,

I'm sorry. I'm sorry for all the wrong ways I've treated you over the past years. I'm sorry for starving you and making you function on little or no energy. I'm sorry for making you drop fat at such a rapid rate. And I'm also sorry for stuffing you with unhealthy food. I'm sorry, stomach, for making you stretch and work overtime to contract and throw up what I stuffed inside you. Thanks for still making that stomach acid to keep me alive, even though I've wasted buckets of it.

I'm sorry, body, for cursing you when you didn't comply with my desires. I'm sorry for scrutinizing you in the mirror, analyzing you from all angles, and wishing you looked different. I'm sorry I wanted you to be something you could never be. I'm sorry for not appreciating all the amazing things you do for me. And I'm sorry for only seeing the bad and never the good.

I want to change. I am changing. God's doing it. I want to stop staring in the mirror and only thinking bad thoughts. I'm trying. Please be patient with me. Forgive me for putting all kinds of unhealthy things inside you and then expecting you to look different. I take full responsibility for what I put in you, and I will be accountable to everything I put in my mouth. No more easy way out. No more making you throw up. I want to make wiser choices about how I give you energy to function.

I know that Jesus is guiding me and healing me and that soon you will look back on these days and be so thankful they're over. But for now, I want to thank you for all the amazing things you do for me. Thank you, legs, for getting me up the Grand Canyon. You amaze me how you work, how each muscle flexes and functions in perfect harmony to get me to places I want to go. Thank you, arms, fingers and hands, for functioning in perfect harmony, for letting me type this letter. How the heck do you do that? I think, and you move. Amazing! Thank you, stomach, for digesting and processing all of the things I put into you and for delivering the energy to places you see fit. Thank you, bloodstream, for carrying all the little molecules and atoms to their designated places and for going to war when foreign objects invade.

Body, it's a wonder how you're still functioning the way you do after all I've put you through. Forgive me? No hard feelings, right? Thanks for understanding, for your patience, grace, and mercy. I resolve to treat you right, and I'll do everything I can to hasten the coming of the day when we can walk together in total healing and freedom. Sorry for getting my emotions all tangled up in how I treat you. I will listen more to the Holy Spirit inside. He'll get us through this. Don't worry. Thanks for listening.

Yours Truly,
The one living inside,
Jessica

Receiving

So many times I had cursed my body, and so many times I had rejected people's compliments. I had to learn to receive affirmations.

Accepting affirmations will challenge your negative thoughts. When my husband has told me I'm beautiful or that he loves me, there were many times I didn't receive it because the voices inside my head disagreed. Once when we were engaged, I told him I had trouble receiving his love and compliments. He knew there was a battle going on for my heart and decided to take aggressive action against the enemy's lies. We sat on the couch, and he told me he loved me over and over and over again. I sat there, very uncomfortable at first, and let it sink in.

At first I wasn't looking into his eyes because I didn't think I deserved his love. I was ashamed. Then I forced myself to look into his eyes, letting my heart be vulnerable and unashamed, receiving all the love he was pouring out. The Holy Spirit descended on us in power, and I wept hard as I let Jesse's and the Holy Spirit's love saturate my being. I had never felt so loved and beautiful in my life.

In another instance, I had fears of Jesse seeing my stomach. Before we were married, we kept ourselves from temptation by setting physical boundaries, specific to us. He hadn't seen me in a bathing suit yet, and I was afraid that when he did, he wouldn't like what he saw. I'd be found out, discovered as a fake, and he would "know" that I wasn't as beautiful as he thought. The fear came up one night when we were driving, and he reached over and put his hand on my stomach. I quickly pushed it away. I didn't want him feeling the bulge. We had just eaten dinner.

At the beginning of our relationship, we decided to be open about every fear we had about getting close to one another. That way we were taking our thoughts captive together and getting to know one another's heart. It kept us from doing things out of insecurity or fear of losing the other person. We wanted to fall in love with each other, not who we were pretending to be.

That night as we sat on the couch, I decided to be open about my fear and said, "Is it OK if my stomach isn't flat?" I know it sounds silly, but it was a fear I had, and it had to be brought into the light. He looked at me, knowing my history, and knew this wasn't a comment to be taken lightly. He put his hand back on my stomach, which made me very uncomfortable—I was so afraid he'd be shocked and disgusted by how "big" it was. I forced myself to let his hand stay there as he said over and over again, "Jessica, I love your stomach, I love your stomach, I love your body, every inch. I love it."

It took everything in my power not to squirm away. I had to let the truth in. I started crying and crying and crying as I received his overwhelming acceptance of me. Led by the Holy Spirit, he then began saying, "It's OK. You're safe. You're safe. You're safe." I wept from such a deep place that I knew my heart was undergoing some serious surgery. And he didn't stop until the Holy Spirit was done.

This was the beginning of knowing that I didn't have to hide any part of myself from Jesse. It was safe for me to be vulnerable. On our wedding night, I didn't have to fear him seeing me for the first time. He had created a safe place for me to be me. He was in love with me, just as I was in love with him. I knew the road would be hard at times, but I knew he desired to fight for my freedom, to create a place where I knew it was safe to reveal every inch of me: personality, quirks, opinions, thoughts, and body.

This is the way Christ loves the church. He loves what He created! He, too, has created a safe place for us to be exactly who we are, not who we want Him to think we are. When we receive Him and His truth, we are freeing ourselves up to be exactly who we were created to be.

Victory!

As your healing continues, it's important to focus not only on the good things about who you are but also on your victories. Every time temptation comes, look at it not as a struggle but as an opportunity to demonstrate that you live in a place of victory. When we celebrate our victories, it teaches us to encourage ourselves instead of always looking for what we did wrong. Your victory may be as simple as being OK with not spending hours at the gym, or having a deep conversation with a friend without feeling anxious. Write about it! Praise God for it!

Focusing on the victory helps cultivate a thankful heart. It's how we stay living in His kingdom. When we thank Him, it takes us into His presence, and we realize where we are: living in victory, seated in the heavenly places right beside Him.

The following describes a victory I had a few months before our wedding:

April 10, 2008

Yay, victory! Yay, victory! Yay, victory! This morning I just had an amazing victory over bulimia! It had been so long since I'd struggled. About ten months purge-free. When I started dating Jesse back in November, the enemy came at me again. I've been fighting the lies with Jesse by my side now; however, I've binged and purged about four different times since we started dating. I've had some incredible victories as well, and I need to document this one:

I feel so overwhelmed with the love of God right now. His mercy and grace are washing over me. I feel so grateful to Him for giving me the victory that I'm moved to tears. I'm in love. So in love with my Savior King! Thank You, Jesus!

Some background: I have a wedding in three months. I've been wanting to "get toned" for the big day. To do this, I need a few rules and guidelines. However, that can be dangerous given my history. It's been interesting, but Jesse and God are helping me stay away from doing it out of fear of being rejected by Jesse. I know that he loves me and the way I look right now, and that if I don't lose a single pound I'll still be secure.

This week I've been off my healthy eating track. Too many dinners out to be a total stickler. I've allowed myself grace. However, grace can easily turn into an all-or-nothing mentality if I'm not careful. This is what just happened.

I took Jesse to the airport early this morning. On the way home , I stopped at the grocery store. I picked up some dried fruit, which used to be something I binged on. Unfortunately, I know how high in calories that stuff is. I never look at the label when I already know it's bad for you. I'd rather live in denial. But I still felt ashamed for doing it.

Anyway, I moved on and went to a job interview. On the drive home, my head began swirling with thoughts like, "You aren't ready to handle a position like that. You wouldn't make a good teacher. It would be too stressful and too much work." I was agreeing with the enemy's lies about my self-worth. I also had no game plan for my day, which added to an even lower sense of self-worth. "I should write, I should study finances, I should go up to San Diego State University and pray for the sick, I should be doing something!" Having too many "I shoulds" and not enough guidance gets very burdensome.

With these subconscious thoughts weighing me down, I walked into the house and went straight to the fridge—anything to satisfy the depression. I opened a container of pasta I had saved from a social gathering. I didn't keep it so I could eat it. I kept it so I wouldn't be wasteful. I kept it so others could eat it. I have trouble throwing away food. I need to get over it because otherwise I turn into a human garbage disposal, which isn't any better.

I forked some greasy pasta into a bowl, put it in the microwave for three minutes, and continued to pick out of the Tupperware as I waited. The ping-pong match began. "What are you doing?"

"It's just pasta. I'll just have one bowl."

"Why? It's not that good anyway. Are you really hungry? Does it satisfy enough to be doing this?"

"You should just keep going and purge. It'll feel so good. No one will have to know. Jesse's gone, and you don't have to tell him."

"What are you doing? Do you really want to keep secrets from Jesse?" I made a quick decision and dumped the huge Tupperware of pasta down the disposal. Yay! Freedom, freedom, freedom, and all the while the enemy was saying, "What are you doing? You're so wasteful. You could've given it to that homeless man on the corner. Wasteful Americans."

The microwave beeped. Do I really want that pasta? I weighed the pros and cons in my head. I thought about what my body really wanted. I realized I wasn't even hungry. I quickly dumped the bowl out into the sink so the enemy couldn't have any more time to tell me why I should change my mind.

Victory! Victory! Victory! O, man! I was so overwhelmed with a sense of victory that I began jumping up and down and praising Jesus out loud in the kitchen. He grabbed me and held me and jumped with me and laughed with me. I began to tear up with gratitude, so thankful that Jesus gave me the grace to do it. He gave me the victory. It was just a matter of whether or not I wanted to take it. I was indescribably full, indescribably satisfied, and overwhelmed with joy. It was as if someone had just taken shackles off my hands and led me out of a dark chamber and into the light.

In that moment, I was also flooded with love for Jesse. I wanted to call him right then and tell him how much I loved him. I wanted to celebrate with him. I pondered why I should feel so in love and realized it was because the alternative decision, to binge and purge, and possibly keep it from him, only created distance between us. It caused me to hide, to pretend. It's like back in the garden. Adam and Eve were ashamed that they were naked and exposed, so they hid. Their relationship with God became distant because of their sin.

Sin and hiding break perfect relationship. Jesse had been fighting with me against these lies and to give in would discredit and dishonor his love for me. It would also discredit God's love for me. The reason we feel distant from God when we sin is the same reason we feel distant from others. We're ashamed, and so we hide, rejecting love and accepting death.

In contrast, it's hard to sin when our eyes are on Him. It was hard for me to choose bulimia when I knew I would have to end up telling Jesse to prevent that horrible feeling that comes with hiding. It was hard for me to choose death when I knew how much God loved me. When our eyes lock on

His, sin looks like a horrifying option. It's when we lose eye contact that we get into trouble.

Thank You, Jesus!

God commands us to "rejoice always" (Philippians 4:4). I used to think this meant, suck it up and put on a fake smile. But this is not a command to hide and pretend. Instead, it's an expression of God's desire for us to have joy. In Bill Johnson's book, *Strengthen Yourself in the Lord,* he explains how this verse is simply God telling us how to have joy: by rejoicing always. "We not only rejoice *because* we have joy—we rejoice in our *pursuit* of joy."

The next time you find yourself lacking joy, try rejoicing. Think lovely thoughts. I guarantee the joy will come.

PART V

BONDING WITH GOD

'Cause I need more than philosophy.
Some god in outer space
doesn't mean anything to me.
Won't you come.

John Mark McMillan

At the beginning of this book, I mentioned how eating disorders, or any type of bondage, are a result of lack of intimacy with God. Intimacy is not the same thing as going to church; it's not reading Christian books, it's not going to Bible studies and getting someone else's revelation, and it's not being a good person. Intimacy only comes from personal encounters with the living God.

At first, I learned how to be intimate with God by hearing how other people interacted with Him. I wanted the nearness they had, so I began to copy what they did in their quiet times. Soon I developed my own private garden with Him. This is my hope for you as I share a few of the practical ways I have built my relationship with this magnificent God.

CHAPTER 32

GOD SPEAKS

BEFORE I begin, I realize that some people reading this book do not yet have a relationship with God. While most people believe there is a God and that there are many ways to Him, the truth is there is only one God and one way: through His Son, Jesus. Entire books (including the Bible) have been written to share the good news of the life He extends to us—but I will sum it up in a few pages.

The Bible is a love story—a story of a loving God pursuing His children. Even when His kids sin—turning from Him and turning to other things—He still pursues them.

Sin is knowing the right thing to do, but not doing it (James 4:17). It rises out of the selfish desires that battle against our soul (James 4:1). Our sin separates us from God. However, this separation is not because God rejects us, but because we reject Him. In the Garden of Eden, Adam and Eve listened to the voice of the enemy and ate from the tree that God had told them not to eat from—the Tree of the Knowledge of Good and Evil.

> [The serpent] said to the woman, "Did God really say, 'You must not eat from any tree in the garden'?" The woman said to the serpent, "We may eat fruit from the trees in the garden, but God did say, 'You must not eat fruit from the tree that is in the middle of the garden, and you must not touch it, or you will die.'" "You will not certainly die," the serpent said to the woman. "For God knows that when you eat of it your eyes will be opened, and you will be like God, knowing good and evil." (Genesis 3:1-5)

The enemy tricked Eve into questioning God's intentions. She was deceived into believing that God was withholding something from her, and so she ate and so did Adam. Suddenly, they awoke to the fact that they were naked. Ashamed and afraid of God, they hid. They went from a perfect life, living in utopia with God, experiencing endless love, pleasure, and peace, to being scared of God. How did this happen? The product of their sin (disobedience) was the ability to evaluate themselves. They were given the knowledge of good and evil. The fruit was like poison to their minds. They no longer simply believed God, but were given a framework by which to evaluate His Word and what He thought about them. Eve suddenly wasn't beautiful simply because "Daddy said so." Now she had the ability to evaluate her beauty and worth based on her own definitions —maybe I'm not so beautiful, I wonder what Adam thinks, she's skinnier than me, etc. . . .

Without truth reigning in their hearts, sin began to kill them from the inside out. "For the wages of sin is death" (Romans 6:23). It causes us to be internally focused—selfish and full of pride, qualities that always end up negatively effecting the world around us.

But God wasn't angry. Instead of turning away from Adam and Eve, the Lord pursued them, calling out to them, "Where are you?"

God always pursues us, even in our sin. But sin gives us a false interpretation of ourselves and Him. We either believe we don't need God (we can make better decisions on our own) and come to the conclusion that He doesn't exist or that His ways are bogus, or we're afraid of His punishment, ashamed of what we've done, and so we hide. But God never hides from us. He is never ashamed.

This picture of the Lord pursuing His bride is repeated all throughout the Bible. Even when it says, "For this reason a man will leave his father and mother and be united to his wife, and they will become one flesh" (Genesis 2:24), God is trying to show us something about His nature. It's not the wife clinging to the man in insecurity. It's the husband, God, in security, cleaving to us, His bride, offering us His undying love and protection, despite our flaws. He is always there, wooing us into His arms, but we must receive this love in order to experience it.

Jesus is love. The Word of God—the truth of His love for us—became flesh and dwelt among us (see John 1:14). God sent us His only son to show us His heart. What did Jesus do on earth? Jesus restored us to the Father who never left us. He brought what religion never could: free life.

Jesus paid the ultimate sacrifice through His death on the cross. He took away all the guilt and shame that sin brought us by showing us that our debts have been cancelled, paid in full. For the wages of sin is death, but the gift of God is eternal life in Christ Jesus our Lord" (Romans 6:23). "Once you were alienated from God and were enemies in your minds because of your evil behavior. But now he has reconciled you by Christ's physical body through death to present you holy in his sight, without blemish and free from accusation" (Colossians 1:21-22).

We don't have to earn God's love. It's free. We don't have to jump through hoops, offering sacrifices again and again to be right in God's eyes. I know I often feel this way. But Jesus became sacrifice for us. We can therefore draw near to God with a clear conscience, free from fear (Hebrews 9:14). "There is no fear in love. But perfect love drives out fear, because fear has to do with punishment" (1 John 4:18). His motives are never to punish us.

And Jesus didn't stay in the grave. He rose from the dead, demonstrating the new life offered to us—dead to sin, alive in Christ. And all we have to do to receive this gift is to say, "Yes! I receive Your grace, Jesus. I want and need Your resurrection power in every area of my life."

Romans 10:9 says, "If you declare with your mouth, 'Jesus is Lord,' and believe in your heart that God raised Him from the dead, you will be saved." Why? Not because you prayed some formulaic prayer, but because you've experienced a revelation of the Father's love and desire to receive Him fully into your life. It has nothing to do with a ticket into heaven (although eternal life naturally extends into the euphoria of heaven) and everything to do with a transformed life, right here, right now. A life filled with the supernatural, blissful love of the Father. A life that naturally extends God's love to everyone around us, creating heaven on earth. "For the grace of God that brings salvation has appeared to all men. It teaches us to say 'No' to ungodliness and worldly passions, and to live self-controlled, upright and godly lives in this present age" (Titus 2:11,12).

Hell is not a place where God sends people to be punished—it was never created for us (Matt 25:41). It's simply a place void of all that God is: love, peace, joy, hope, etc. . . . . (2 Thessalonians 1:9). It's what we choose when we reject Him. God in His perfect love offers us this choice because without a choice it wouldn't be true love. It would be slavery. And for choice to exist, there must be an alternative to choose. Something as compelling as love. Something that looks like love and life but leads to death. Forced love is not love at all. It's bondage.

God doesn't want mindless zombies in heaven—people forced to worship Him all day because they can't help it. He wants friends.

Life is ultimately about an epic battle over the hearts of mankind. God pursues and so does the enemy, masquerading as an angel of light, mixing truth with false assumptions, just like in the garden. It's up to us to decide whose voice we will follow.

So, are you ready to enter into an abundant life? To live the life you were designed to live, free from the bondage of choosing the things that destroy you? Free to live by the Spirit? Then repeat after me: "Jesus, forgive me. I'm tired of hiding. I believe that You died on the cross to free me from the weightiness of my sins and lead me into a relationship with You. Jesus, You are Lord. I want to live with You and know You all the days of my life. I know that life with You is far better than life without You, and right now, I surrender all of me. Take my life, Lord. I want You. I am Yours!"

Praise God! The angels are rejoicing with God in heaven over you! You are a new creation! The old has gone, and the new has come (2 Corinthians 5:17). How good does it feel to rest in God's embrace? Now let's learn how to grow in intimacy with Him. He is so excited to unfold all of His mysteries to you.

God Speaks

God speaks to us in a number of ways. The following is by no means a complete list of ways in which He speaks. Instead, I want to share a few simple ways that helped me get started on my journey to hearing from Him. He speaks to me most frequently through reading the Word and journaling, stream of thought (the still, small voice), pictures in my imagination (visions), and encountering His love in rest and worship. The latter will be covered in the following chapter.

His Word

I remember as a new Christian asking my pastor how to tell if the voices I heard in my head were God's, the enemy's, or mine. He told me that knowing the difference comes from spending time with Him, from learning how He sounds, first by reading His Word. Reading the Word establishes truth in our hearts, allowing us to discern His voice.

I made reading His Word a priority in my life. Every morning, same time, same place, I would pick up the Word and my journal and start reading a chapter.

I began the practice of reading the Word with Him by asking Him questions and writing them down in my journal. I would then wait to hear the answer. It's a great way to actively read. Reading actively along with Him helps keep our minds from wandering and also helps us build an actual relationship with Him. Reading becomes about intimacy rather than a religious duty.

Once I made reading the Word a habit in my life, I began gaining a better understanding of God's character and could, therefore, distinguish how He speaks to me.

As the written Word transforms our hearts, we have a greater capacity to hear His spoken Word. He speaks to the things that have been planted through the Word and calls them forth by His voice. It's as if our hearts now have a receiver to pick up the correct sound waves around us. He's always speaking. We just need to get our receivers tuned in to His voice. Reading His Word prepares us to receive.

I love His Word. It brings me so much life. Second Timothy 3:16 says, "All scripture is God-breathed." It's been made alive by the very breath of God. He loves revealing things to me. Reading the Word with Holy Spirit is like going on a hunt for buried treasure with Him. When we find the treasure, the revelation, it goes down into our inmost parts and fills us up, completely satisfying our needs. Jeremiah 15:16 says, "When Your words showed up, I ate them—swallowed them whole. What a feast! What delight I took in being Yours, O God, God-of-the-Angel-Armies!" (The Message).

One morning I was so excited to get up and read His Word, to receive His servings of love, that I wrote a poem:

January 19, 2006

My Lover Feeds Me

> *Each morning I wake as He kisses me,*
> *And I melt into His love all the more.*
> *Romanced by His ruddy, rich history,*
> *And wond'ring bout words and what's more,*
> *He feeds me breakfast, the words that I need.*
> *He draws me to Him and I move to his lead.*
> *I open, invite, get hit with light,*
> *Amazed that He chooses to bless me with sight,*

To understand proverbs hanging heavy from strings
Of the harp as the pages leak honey sweet things.
My heart breathing in as I'm racing the lines,
Or sometimes I'm slowly retracing the lines,
I'm feasting on truth, and I love every bit,
Slurping down every drop of the life I can get.

Broken yet blossomed, I like it just fine.
He cleanses my lips with hot coals that we mined.
A meal that is pure, it's His gift and it's mine.
The Truth and the Life,
* it's on these things I dine.*

I don't always feel like reading the Word, but sometimes all it takes is reminding myself how good it tastes—declaring, "O God, thank You for Your Word. It brings life to my very bones. Thank You for what You are going to show me today."

Always remember, you are free. God is not judging you based on how much you read or how well you remember it. He just wants to bond with you. Knowing this frees us up from feeling as if reading is a duty. We are free to enjoy His Word. Because I know I am free, I sometimes divert from my reading track and read a Psalm. I read until something in my spirit leaps. Other times, God actually tells me not to read but to simply be with Him or journal.

The most important thing is relationship—building intimacy and growing in your identity. Studying is good, but if your sole purpose for reading is to study as you would for a class, you've missed the point. There is no test. God wants to be known, not studied.

I used to think that being a good Christian meant studying to have all the answers. That way, when the time came, I could make good arguments for why God is real. I read the verse, "Always be prepared to give an answer to everyone who asks you to give the reason for the hope that you have" (1 Peter 3:15) and took it to mean: "Study up! You've got to be ready to have a good argument."

But Matthew 10:19-20 says, "Do not worry about what to say or how to say it. At that time you will be given what to say, for it will not be you speaking, but the Spirit of your Father speaking through you." Being ready means be connected to the Spirit. Be in relationship with Him. Be full of Him! The Spirit welling up inside you will do the work.

The Still, Small Voice

The most common way God speaks is in the place where we hear ourselves think. That's why many people mistake God's voice for their own thoughts. There, God's voice is "still" and "small" and easy to miss. It does not boom. It does not shake. God does speak audibly at times. I have never heard Him speak to me this way (though I can't wait to hear Him when He does), but I've heard it's impossible to miss.

On the other hand, learning to discern the still, small voice takes practice. I learned to trust that when I asked Him questions and heard answers in my head, it was Him. If it wasn't, I trusted that He was big enough to correct me. If it lined up with the Word, it was Him. If it brought me life, it was Him. And while I can't list more ways to help you judge whether or not you hear His voice, something that might help is that if you hear something that you probably couldn't think of or say yourself, it's probably Him.

Sometimes He doesn't answer the way we think He should. For instance, one time I asked Him if I should get to work on writing. He said, "I love you."

"Yeah, I know God, but do You want me to write right now?" I could have missed this voice if I wasn't really listening. I could have waited for the yes or no answer. But God told me what I needed to hear. He knew I was trying to earn His love by being productive. I needed to know that He loved me no matter what I did. "I love you" was the answer to the real question.

Other times God speaks to our spirits through impressions. For instance, many times I've felt as if Jesse is about to call me, and right then he calls. God's impressions are the same way. Recently, Jesse and I were on our way to a party and had written down a list of things we felt God speaking to us about people we were going to meet: clothing, names, appearances, injuries, and so forth. We call this treasure hunting, and to learn more you'll have to read *The Ultimate Treasure Hunt* by Kevin Dedmon. We didn't find everyone on our list, but the next day we were heading out, and I was changing purses. I felt like I was supposed to put the list in my new purse. It wasn't a voice, just an impression. We ended up encountering two people on our list: a woman with a broken toe and a woman with an arm in a sling. Both women were healed instantly after we prayed!

God is always speaking. If you position yourself to hear Him, you'll hear.

Visions

The simplest way to describe a vision is to show you one: Picture a white house in meadow. Can you see it? That's what a vision looks like. You see it in your imagination, with the eyes of your heart. You don't have to have your eyes closed to see them, and like the still, small voice, they are often fleeting and easy to miss. Again, this is because people expect God to be more obvious. We end up mistaking visions for our own imagination.

The other day I was asking God for an encouraging word for a friend. I saw a very subtle picture of a white rabbit. I could have easily disregarded this image as something foolish, but honestly, why on earth would I start picturing a white rabbit? So I decided to stop rejecting the image and asked God to show me more. I thought of the white rabbit in *Alice in Wonderland* who shouts, "I'm late! I'm late! I'm late!" I felt that God wanted to tell my friend that he was worried about always being late but that God says he is right on time.

I thought I was probably making it up, but I stepped out in faith and shared anyway. He said, "Oh my gosh! You have no idea. All day long my number one worry is that I am always behind on all my projects. I always feel like I'm late and can't catch up."

The word about him being right on time lifted a huge weight off his shoulders. He was blessed beyond measure because only God could have known that about him. And all of this came about because I trusted a faint picture of a silly white bunny.

There are a myriad of other ways God speaks to His children: through creation, unusual circumstances, unusual coincidences, dreams, testimonies, our senses, prophetic words. Learning to hear His voice is necessary if you want to break off the chains of bondage. It's a necessary connection between heaven and earth, where heaven's reality becomes realized in our minds and manifested all around us. Connecting to His heart through His voice is the subject of the next chapter.

CHAPTER 33

THE PERSONS OF GOD

WHEN I say "persons" of God, I am not referring to the Godhead: Father, Son, and Holy Spirit. Although it is important to learn how to relate to all three manifestations of the same God, this is not the subject of this chapter. Instead, with "persons" I am referring to the different characters that God portrays. Just as you and I can be a friend, a mother or father, or a lover, so can God. My friends relate to me differently than my husband does, and my children will relate to me differently than my friends do, yet I am the same person.

In the same way, we can learn to relate to God's heart from different perspectives: as His friend, His precious child, or His lover. While there are many manifestation and names for God, these are the three I discuss here.

God As Friend

As I began to discern God's voice, I learned that He doesn't just love me. He likes me, and He really enjoys my company. I made it a point to spend time with Him during daily activities. The car is a great place to practice this: "Hey, God, thanks for driving with me. What's on Your mind lately?"

The conversations seemed one way at first, but soon I began hearing His responses. The truth is, He is always speaking to me. I just had to trust in His ability to make Himself heard. It was so freeing to know that I didn't have to come to Him only with my problems. I am not a project. I am a friend of God, and He wants to hang out with me—the only agenda: Have fun.

As we began interacting in normal, daily activities, I learned that He is incredibly witty and at times downright hilarious. One time I asked Him how He made the palm tree I was admiring. He responded with a Jim Carrey impersonation. In the outtakes from *Liar Liar*, Carrey is performing his usual antics in the courthouse when he constructs a goose out of foil, remarking, "A goose!" God did the same thing in my mind with His palm tree, and it was the funniest thing I ever saw. God was speaking my language, and it made me feel so close to Him, so known. We had a great time laughing together.

Don't be surprised if God cracks jokes that only you would understand. His voice is not restricted to Bible verses. Remind yourself that He really is right next to you, not up in a cloud. He loves hanging out with you, and if you invite Him into your day, He will take you on great adventures. Go on dates with Him. Go on walks in the park. When you're with Him, you will start to notice the beauty in things you never had before. It's so good to delight in God. And it's OK to waste our lives on Him. I used to think that if I just tried harder, I could be a better Christian. If I led Bible studies or told someone about Jesus or fed the homeless, God would be proud of me, and I would feel accomplished as a spiritual person. I was so caught up in the "Go and make disciples" verse that I missed the whole love story that involves a God coming to earth, not to tell us what to do but to be close to us, to show us the way to intimacy.

There's a reason why the Word says, "My yoke is easy and my burden is light" (Matthew 11:30). He would rather we spend all day just lying on the floor with Him than trying to earn His love by telling someone about Jesus. We can't earn His love. He didn't put that yoke on us.

There have been seasons in my life marked by spending hours on the floor, just being with Him and resting in His love. Those have been the seasons when I am so alive and full that ministry just happens. I can't help but fall in love with the people around me, because I begin to see them as God sees them. I hear the words He speaks over them. I am no longer self-conscious. I am free.

God As Daddy

I remember the first time I called God "Daddy." I was deep in worship, thoroughly enjoying Him, when I said, "Oh, Daddy, I love You!" Then I thought, *Wait a second. Is that OK? It sounds so irreverent.* But then I realized, *What father doesn't love the sound of his precious child calling out, "Daddy, Daddy, Daddy!"*

God loves it when I call Him Daddy. Even Jesus called God Daddy in Mark 14:36 when He said, "Abba, Father, everything is possible for You." Abba is the Hebrew word for daddy.

For the longest time, people would speak over me, "I really feel like God just wants you to know Him as Father." And I thought I did, but as I continued to pursue Him, I realized I didn't fully understand how much He loved me as Dad. I perceived Him as a distant God who was only involved in my life when I was good, and even then He observed me from a distance.

The truth is, daddies delight in their kids. They can't get enough of them. Picture a dad, in love with his child, tossing him into the air—both of them laughing—buying him a toy *simply because*, holding him and rocking him because he hurt his knee, kissing him on the forehead as he tucks him in at night. That is our God. He is enamored with you and treats you as His beloved child.

> *But God himself took charge of his people, took Jacob on as his personal concern. He found him out in the wilderness, in an empty, windswept wasteland. He threw his arms around him, lavished attention on him, guarding him as the apple of his eye. He was like an eagle hovering over its nest, overshadowing its young, then spreading its wings, lifting them into the air, teaching them to fly...God lifted him onto the hilltops, so he could feast on the crops in the fields... Fine Bashan rams, high-quality wheat, and the blood of grapes: you drank good wine!*
>
> (Deuteronomy 32:10-14) (The Message)

This portrays God as a very hands-on father, loving, protecting, nurturing, teaching, and providing only the best for His kids. He is not stingy. He does not withhold things to punish us or because we didn't earn them, but only because He knows the perfect time and place to meet the desires of our heart. He waits with eager expectation as He leads us to a place where we can receive what He wants to give us. Matthew 7:11 says, "If you, then, though you are evil, know how to give good gifts to your children, how much more will your Father in heaven give good gifts to those who ask him!"

Ask God to help you know Him as Daddy. All of us have had less-than-perfect dads. Some of us formulate our perception of God based on what kind of father we had. Was he quick to anger? Distant? Absent? Did he show love by giving you things instead of spending time with you? Did he withhold gifts from you because he was concerned about money?

God is none of those things. He is patient, slow to anger, and abounding in love. He is generous and loves giving good gifts to His kids. His love never changes, nor does His distance from you. He is always right next to you. What may change is your perception of His nearness as you learn to commune with Him.

Yell out, "Daddy!" over and over until your heart gets it. Declare that He is a good dad. Determine that while your earthly father may have failed, God never does. And once you learn to be His little girl or boy, your childlike trust and faith will lead you into encounters with Him that you could never imagine—encounters that will heal your broken heart.

God As a Lover

Once I began grabbing hold of God as a daddy, He began revealing Himself to me as my lover. I remember texting a friend, and when I asked what he was doing, he responded, "Just worshiping my lover."

Lover? I thought. *What an odd thing to call God.* Especially coming from a man. But I desperately wanted that nearness.

The key to becoming whole is taking our desires to be loved and pursued to God, first and foremost. We need to open ourselves to *His* love and romance (yes, I said romance) before we can fully receive it from any person. His romance is not the perverted kind the world boasts about. It's perfect and pure. It is a love flowing out of a heart that has been captivated by you.

Can you relate to the desire to be romanced (especially if you are a woman)? God put that there. Proverbs 19:22 says, "What a man (human) desires is unfailing love" (parenthesis mine). No man can give you a perfect, unfailing love. Only God can. No man can define you or tell you who you are. Only God can. He's the one who made you. He knows who you are better than you know yourself.

The world tells us that if we're not being pursued, there's something wrong with us or we're missing something. Not true. The Bible says, "Delight yourself in the Lord and He will give you the desires of your heart" (Psalm 37:4). He will meet all of your desires, including the one to be pursued, seen, delighted in, and loved.

Have you ever thought of God as a lover? As a romancer? Read Song of Solomon. Your heart will come alive with His words of romance over you.

Song of Solomon 4:7 says, "All beautiful you are my darling; there is no flaw in you. Come with me from Lebanon my bride." He calls us His bride. We are pure and white to Him, and He wants to pursue us, cherish us, and protect us as a husband should. "You are a garden locked up, my treasure my bride, you are a spring enclosed, a sealed fountain."

The woman (us) then says, "Let my lover come into His garden and taste its choice fruits." She's inviting Him in. She knows who she is and that what she has to offer is "choice grade," perfect and wonderful. Then the lover (God) says, "I have come into my garden, my treasure my bride."

It might be foreign or odd to you to read these passages as an interaction between you and God. But you must understand, calling God *lover* is not a sexual thing. It's an intimate thing. He's meeting us in the depths of our desire to be seen and known—to be beautiful to someone.

God wants to take you on a journey of being romanced by Him. He wants to show you how to guard your heart so that it is reserved first for Him and second for the mate He created for you. He wants to show you how precious and pure you are, because He has cleansed you and made you whole. He wants you to come to the revelation that what you have to offer Him is choice grade, perfect and without flaw in His sight.

You are all He wants. You. Just you. He doesn't see your flaws. He sees a beautiful creation. You have stolen His heart, and He can't get enough of you. He longs to unfold His mysteries to you and to lavish His love on you, but He's waiting for your invitation.

Have you ever thought that because we are made in His image and have the desire to be pursued, maybe God has this desire as well? He longs to be pursued by you. He's not lacking anything, yet He delights in your pursuit of Him. Even your weak love overwhelms Him.

I made a decision to let God romance me, and my life has never been the same. I am lovesick. I can't get enough of Him. I can't stop singing to Him, singing about Him, and laughing at the simple thought that He adores me. When I behold His adoration of me, I can't help but well up with a tearful smile. And in the moments when I'm striving or I forget His love, all I have to do is pause and let His delight wash over me. I enjoy Him and am confident in His enjoyment over me, even when I'm not doing anything. He simply enjoys me!

The same is true for you. Make a decision to have God be your one obsession, your heart's desire, your lover. Song of Solomon is a good place to start. Let Him speak His love for you as He tells you that you are all He wants. Once glance of your eye overwhelms Him!

One of my favorite ways of just "being" and letting Him romance me is through music. I get alone in my room and put on my iPod (see appendix A for music ideas if you need some) and just start singing to Him and meeting with Him face-to-face. I remember the first time I danced with Him. I was listening to a song called "Dance with Me," and God said, "Can I have this dance?" I stood up and held out my hands, positioned my head on His shoulder, and started swaying back and forth. I was so content in His arms.

Doing something like this may seem weird to you, but God loves a childlike heart—a heart that trusts in what we cannot see with our natural eye. I had the best time that day, simply being romanced by my lover. Now dancing with Him is something I do often in my secret place with Him.

My Season on the Floor

Later, in 2007 I went through a season where I spent hours on the floor, worshipping and receiving. Every day I came back to the same place in my room, put on the iPod, and just lay there. I would fix my thoughts on Him. This will take practice, as it's easy for our minds to wander. Don't get mad at yourself when it does. It may help to keep a notepad nearby to write down errands and things that are distracting you. Also, it's always good to keep a journal to record what you feel God speaking to you.

As I began this practice of lying on the floor with "soaking" worship music, God met me in such a powerful way that it has changed my life. I began to let His presence, His glory, saturate me as I lay, receiving every drop of His love.

Sometimes I would just meditate on a phrase: "O Holy Spirit, show me the wonder of Your great love." Other times, if I couldn't feel His nearness, I'd yell into the air, "God! Where are You?!" Honesty feels so good. He already knows what's in our heart anyway. What's the point of trying to pretend? And even though He hears our thoughts, He enjoys us expressing ourselves with Him. That's what people in relationship do. They interact.

I had some wild encounters with God on the floor. Sometimes I'd literally be shaking under the power of Holy Spirit. I felt as if electricity was running through my body and knew the angels were doing surgery on me. Sometimes I'd feel Him so close I thought I would die if I opened my eyes and saw His glory. Other times I'd drift off into encounters with Him through visions. I'd imagine myself running through the hills of Eden with Him or lying in the shade of a big tree beside a purple river, letting Him skip around me.

His love is so powerful. It's not just a nice notion. It will shake you from the inside out if you let it in. One minute you might be weeping, the next drunk with laughter. This happens to me quite often. Simply thinking about how good He is and shouting, "Thank You! Thank You! Thank You, Jesus!" often sends me into bouts of laughter where my joy is so intense I'm burning up with His presence. I collapse to the ground, shaking and laughing hysterically because my joy can't be contained. It's so amazing to experience such powerful emotions after being so numb for so many years. It's the life I had been missing.

Spending so much time with Him lit me up in a way I cannot describe. I had become His beautiful bride. Here is one of the many poems that effortlessly flowed out of me while I was in the depths of His love.

September 25, 2007

O Daddy O Lover, O Daddy O Lover.
You satisfy my innermost being. You satisfy my yearning soul. My soul yearns for a generation to be fired up for You! To understand the depth of Your Great Love. To encounter it, feel it pulsing through every vein.

I Am a Torch
I am a torch,
Lord, these flames are for You.
I am Your torch, burn is all I can do.
Can't You see how You've killed
The me that once lived?
But You knew this would happen, You know what You did.
You came and You set, my heart all ablaze,
And now I can't help but waste all my days,
just worshipping, loving, and crying to You.
Just weeping, and loving, the me inside You.
Cause it's You inside me that makes me come undone
And I dance, I've become an undignified one.
My heart and Yours meld, and I feel what You feel
I see what You see, I see truth, I see real.
And I burn 'cause I long for this world just to see,
The me inside You and the You inside me.

Then "O God!" Overwhelmed, I can't take any more.
I collapse and I weep from my spot on the floor.
O God! This can't be! God it's not OK!
For my friends to not know You, Your Love and Your Way.
No, O God! No! O God, please just send,
Your love to melt them.
Will these tears ever end?
But they do,
I get up,
and I burn and I stand.
In the midst of the darkness, O Dad, take my hand!
A vessel I am, of Your love burning bright.
I will go to the end, I will burn thru the night!
And now my one prayer's that You keep my heart soft,
to prevent the frustration and keep sight aloft.
O unashamed love! O unending grace!
I just want You now. I just want Your face.
Without You I die, without Love I can't be.
I am only a torch, with You inside me.
Keep burning away the things that aren't right.
Till all that I am is a vessel of light.
Till these aren't my words, and these aren't my feet,
these aren't my hands, they're not my tears I weep.
O Daddy O Lover, the One I adore,
I don't want to see me or this flesh anymore!
O come! Lord, just come! I can't see, my heart's tore!
I'm a mess I'm a mess, back on this stupid floor.
I'm a mess and I cry and I don't even care,
'Cause You wreck me, You fix me, and brush through my hair.
I'm broken yet burning. These two thoughts collide,
And I'm caught in the wake of the me that just died.
And I watch as she drifts, away through the blue.
And I stand and I burn, this is all I can do.
I am a torch, You called me by name.
I am Your torch.
A desperate flame.

I share this to encourage you that, yes, it is possible. No matter how far away from God you feel right now, know that I was once there, too. And I still have bad days when I believe the enemy's lies, and I don't feel close to Him. But I simply look back on these poems—I remember the words spoken over me, the encounters I've had with Him—and I remind myself that His nearness is always available.

CHAPTER 34

GOD AS MY HUSBAND

There's gonna be a wedding
It's the reason that I'm living,
To marry the Lamb

Tim Reimherr

KNOWING God as my husband came when I let Him be my number one love. I stopped dating when I came back to the Lord in 2003. I knew I didn't want to keep giving my heart away to those who were undeserving. I didn't want to keep practicing divorce by breaking up and getting back together. I trusted that God would lead me to my husband at the right time.

As 2007 rolled on, I started having thoughts about a certain man. I was twenty-five and felt as if marriage was just around the corner. However, I wanted it to be God's will, not just a crush. I was having such a wonderful season of intimacy with God. I didn't know what to do with these thoughts. I kept asking God to take them away, but I kept thinking about him.

One weekend I was at a friend's house where a pastor had been invited to share with us about being led by the Spirit. We had a time when we closed our eyes and walked through an encounter with the Holy Spirit. We asked Him to show us the things that were keeping us from walking in the fullness of carrying His Spirit. I was on my knees in a very private place with Him, although the room was full. I asked what I needed to let go of. First He mentioned my grip on the gym. He wanted me to be OK with changing my routine if He wanted to spend more time with me in the morning instead of having me rushing off to workout. With tears I said, "OK, God." I only wanted Him. Nothing else.

The next thing He said changed me forever. He said, "What about your husband?" A rush of thoughts flashed through my head as I pictured the rest of my life without a husband, without giving birth to the babies I so desperately wanted in the future, spending the rest of my life with just Him and me. I knew this wasn't a question to be taken lightly. As I weighed the options, I knew what I really wanted. God and God alone. I cried, "OK, God! You and me!" And as I shouted this through tears, somewhere deep inside a dam broke, and I cried the messiest cry I have ever cried. I sacrificed my future husband on the altar that night. It was the most painful, yet freeing and intimate thing I've ever done with God.

As I lay in the weight of His presence for hours afterwards, unable to get up, I realized He could very well resurrect the idea of marriage if He wanted to, but like Abraham with Isaac, He was after my heart. Did I trust Him? Did I know that He was good, or did I think that He was trying to punish me or have me live a horrible life without a husband? Did I trust that whatever He had for me was going to be the best?

Afterwards, I assumed my thoughts about this man would go away, but a few days later they came back.

September 29, 2007

> *Good morning, Jesus. Here I am again in a place where I need You to come swallow my drifting thoughts. God, why does my heart betray me? Why am I back here, killing this thing over and over again? Why won't it just stay on the altar?*

I couldn't stop thinking about him, even though I tried; and God began showing me that this was the man He wanted to give me.

Jesse and I got married July 19, 2008. God gave me the most amazing gift I've ever been given: one of His own sons. The story of our love is another book entirely, one that we might one day write together. Our journey of dating, engagement, and now marriage has been incredible because of one thing: intimacy with the Father.

When we started dating, I felt the weight of emotions that go along with the two becoming one. At first I was overwhelmed with humility that God would honor me by trusting me with another person's heart. Then, of course, I had to get over all of the fears that arose as I wondered, *If he knew X about me, would he still love me?* I had to get over my fears about my body, food, and cooking food for him. It has been a learning process. I have shared a few of those experiences with you in previous chapters.

Because we continue to fight the lies together, I have been freer in my body and my eating habits than I ever have been. God has opened me up to a whole new realm of vulnerability. While very difficult and uncomfortable at times, the healing has been so liberating.

Being completely open with God and one another has brought Jesse and me into incredible unity. Whenever I hear the old voices saying "You're fat," or "He's gonna fall out of love with you if you eat that and gain weight" or "You can't eat that in front of him. He'll judge you," I need to disagree with the lies.

Secondly, if I hear the same lie more than once, I share it with Jesse. Instead of whining and saying, "I'm so fat. Do you think I'm fat?" I stand on truth and say, "Jesse, I know you love me just the way I am, but I'm really struggling in my mind right now regarding my body. Could you encourage me and pray with me?" I need to remember that I am loved no matter what shape my body is in. If I go up or down a few sizes, Jesse can never tell the difference anyway.

Sometimes I simply ask, "Am I beautiful?"

No matter how many times he says that I am, I still need to hear it over and over again. But I also realize that I cannot depend on his compliments to sustain me. Only God's truth stands. I owe it to Jesse and myself to fight my own battles and to ask for help when I need it instead of complaining.

As Jesse and I continue our journey together in marriage, only intimacy with the Father brings that deep unity we long for. If we only relied on each other, we would burn out. We need to stay connected to His voice at all times. He is the one who defines us.

God's Presence Is Where Beauty Comes From

A Word for the Woman

I share all this to say that no man can ever define you or be the one to make you feel secure or beautiful. Jesse makes me feel beautiful and secure, yes, but it must come from God first. You can't earn love by having a perfect body. You can only receive it freely.

The world has taught us to use our bodies to earn love. The result is that we end up with men who don't treat us the way we desire to be treated. We seduce men by walking a certain way, dressing a certain way, and carrying ourselves a certain way. (I don't care how innocent you think you are. You know what you're doing when you put on that little tank top and skinny jeans. You're trying to look appealing.) But the problem is, if we're trolling for men with our boobs, butts, or sexy outfits, we are fishing for them by arousing their sex drive, which is stimulated predominantly by sight. And guess what kind of men we catch when we fish with that kind of bait? It's probably not the kind of guy who will give you the respect you desire.

In Kris Vallotton's book, *Purity: The New Moral Revolution,* he explains this phenomenon from a man's perspective. Kris writes, "It may feel great to receive attention and admiration from men when you put your body on display. But you need to know or remember that this admiration is totally superficial. It is the same kind of admiration that they would have for any other beautiful *object.*"

If we want to be loved and respected by men, then we need to carry ourselves in a way that portrays that message. I'm not saying that we need to be nuns or dress in dorky clothes. There are plenty of ways to be fashionable without showing off parts of us that aren't for sale. As Kris writes, "There's a huge difference between looking pretty and being sexy."

While using our bodies to attract men may feel like power, it is actually revealing of our weakness—we're not strong enough to take a stand for our virtues. The stronger we are, and the more love and respect we have for ourselves, the more we'll portray that in the way we carry ourselves. The kind of men we attract will be the kind with the virtues we've always hoped for. Yes, there *are* men out there who have high standards, who are fighting to stay pure for their future wives. But we're not doing them any favors by dressing the ways we do.

If you want a man who will respect you, you'll never get him by stimulating his sex drive. As I've said before, you wouldn't want a man to fall in love with just your body anyway. Beauty fades. Proverbs 31 says beauty is fleeting. God warns in Ezekiel 16:15 not to put our trust in beauty. First Peter 3:2-4 also teaches, "Your beauty should not come from outward adornment, such as braided hair and the wearing of gold jewelry and fine clothes. Instead, it should be that of your inner self, the unfading beauty of a gentle and quiet spirit, which is of great worth in God's sight." This verse is not saying you shouldn't wear makeup or jewelry, or that you should be quiet. No. Be you, a you who is at rest with who she is, fashion or no fashion. Being at rest in God's presence is where beauty comes from.

To help portray my point, here is an excerpt from the book *Captivating* by John and Stasi Eldredge.

> *Janet is twenty-one. She was on the dance team in high school. Small and petite with a fabulous figure. Unlike so many women in that world of competitive beauty, she escaped an eating disorder. But she runs five to ten miles a day. She watches what she eats. She's able to wear the cutest clothes and yet…when you're with her, your heart does not rest. Her beauty impresses, but it does not invite. The reason is simple: She is striving. She is a perfectionist (an extra two pounds is a crisis; a pimple a disaster). Her beauty feels tenuous, shaky. It is not flowing from her heart. It's almost as if it's forced, from the outside, through discipline and fear.*
>
> *June is one of the most beautiful women we have ever met. We encountered her a few years ago while doing a retreat on the coast of North Carolina. Her hair was long, swept up loosely and held by decorative combs. She wore unique, dangly earrings, and pretty flowing skirts. Her eyes sparkled when she laughed, which she did often, and her smile lit up the room. She was clearly in love with her husband, her face adoring as she gazed at him. June was at rest with herself, at home in who she was. Talking with her, just being with her, made us feel more at rest with ourselves as well. Her spacious, beautiful soul invited others to come, to be, to taste and see that the Lord is good, whatever was happening in your life. She wept at the retreat. She laughed at the retreat. She was gloriously alive and in love with the God of the Universe.*
>
> *And June was about seventy-five years old.*
>
> *What is the difference between these two women? Rest. June's beauty flows from a heart at rest. (page 132-133)*

"A heart at peace gives life to the body, but envy rots the bones" (Proverbs 14:30).

God's presence is where beauty comes from. When you become captured by His gaze, romanced by His love, buried in the folds of His robe, you will know who you are. You will be fully alive—full of peace and overflowing joy.

You must know who you are before you can ever give yourself away, before you can be completely loved and completely loving. You are not your body. You are a beautiful spirit waiting to bust out of her walls of fear and shame. The healing is available. God is ready and willing to take you on a miraculous journey of falling in love with Him. The question is, are you willing to receive His truth?

CHAPTER 35

I CAN LIVE AND EAT WITHOUT FEAR!

AT seventeen, I was head-deep in anorexia. By twenty-one, bulimia ruled my life. Just four short months after that, God encountered me, and I began the road to recovery. I am twenty-eight now. It has been a long but powerful road.

During the first months of recovery, my bingeing and purging went from a couple of times a day to once a week. As I learned to use the tools set before me, I made goals for myself to see how long I could go without bingeing. It took me forever to break through that week barrier. A part of me still wanted to hold on to the disorder, and I would sabotage my own goal, giving in the day before the week was up. But by using all the tools mentioned in this book, I slowly started to see the truth. I began pulling away from my unhealthy coping mechanisms.

As I learned to recognize hunger signals and pull away for the eating disorder, my weight fluctuated, which at times was scary. I had tried to control my weight for so long that it took some time to even out. When I was too thin, my metabolism slowed down, and my body attempted to gain weight by sending me intense food cravings. As I began eating intuitively, I went above my natural weight for a short time. But eventually my body found its "set point weigh,t" which is where I am the healthiest. It's where my body genetically wants to be, and it resists any attempts to go lower or higher.

It's so freeing to no longer try to force my body into an unrealistic ideal. I embrace my body type and know that we were not all made to look the same, even though the magazines try to tell us otherwise. I am not overweight, as I feared I would become when this journey began. I am happy, healthy, and free.

Because my body is no longer unnaturally thin, it doesn't fight back and scream out with intense cravings to binge. The binges and purges slowed to once every few months, until now, as I write this, I have gone almost two years without a single purge. From time to time, I've used food as a coping mechanism but rarely and definitely not as dramatically as going to the grocery store and stuffing my face. Instead I choose to be open. I no longer clutch my emotions and fears with crossed arms. I choose to bring them into the light where they can get flooded with truth.

The White Rose

At the beginning of recovery, a friend of mine had a vision for me. She said she saw a beautiful white flower bud. And as she watched, it began to open, but before it could open, my hand reached over and clamped it shut, preventing it from blossoming. That vision felt so true. I knew it was me. I didn't want to keep closing myself off, but I didn't know if I could be any different. I did know, however, that if I remained closed with my feelings bound inside, I would die.

Since recovery, the biggest changes I see are in my relationships with friends, with God, and with food. I no longer hide behind food or isolate myself behind my fear of rejection. I don't leave parties early or turn down dinner offers. I am able to fully engage with people's hearts because I am no longer distracted by the swarm of thoughts about food and my body. The storm in my head has died.

I also no longer feel as if everything in my life needs to be perfectly presentable. When hosting people in my home, I am able to be at peace, even if people are running late or the meal doesn't turn out as planned. I rarely get anxious about making sure everyone's happy and impressed. I let go. These things don't matter. What matters is being present and connected to the ones I love. I'm able to be more flexible and spontaneous and don't freak out if something doesn't go the way I'd pictured in my mind.

The best part is I am able to give and receive true love. I am in touch with what's really going on inside my heart and share it freely, no longer feeling as if I'm just putting on a smile to hide the turmoil inside. Because of this, I am able to offer my true opinions and not just agree with everyone so I'll appear easygoing and likeable. Sometimes it's an effort to pause and think about how I truly feel. But now that I am able to be more vulnerable and receive love, I am confident about sharing my heart if I've been hurt. I no longer stuff everything down and try to convince myself that it's my problem to face alone. We need each other.

My relationship with Daddy God continues to grow. I no longer feel as if I have to earn His love or that I am a disappointment to Him if I mess up, although the lies do try to attack me from time to time. It no longer feels as if He's some God in outer space. I know His nearness. I know He is always proud of me, always patient with me, and wants nothing more than for me to hang out with Him. I have captivated His heart, and He has captured mine. I am at rest in who I am as His beloved daughter, and the joy I have from this freedom surpasses anything I've ever experienced. Laughter and goofiness pour out of me like streams of liquid freedom.

My relationship with food is dramatically different, of course. Food is no longer my enemy. I don't count calories, and I don't have rules about what I can't eat. I recognize hunger signals and eat accordingly. If I'm craving sweets, I let myself have something. I stop when I'm full and almost never feel guilty about leaving food on my plate or having seconds. Every now and then the shame comes in, but I try to be quick about recognizing the lies.

I take good care of my body. I enjoy being active and working out, but I'm not obsessed with the gym and don't freak out about skipping a routine workout. I eat food that I know is nutritious and healthy—that's normally what my body craves anyway—but I don't restrict myself from ordering a burger when I'm in the mood.

Am I perfect? No. As Jesse can attest to, there are days when the lies feel heavy, loud and consuming. Sometimes I just need to cry and share. I need help. But eventually I get back to knowing the truth. I am a free and beautiful daughter, and I can truly live and eat without fear.

March 2006
Now Friends Feel Close

If you never knew me,
I now can tell you why:
My heart was locked behind a wall,
Although I wasn't shy.

I worked overtime to keep it in,
Not knowing it was strange,
And not sure how

To venture out,
I longed for you
To change.
My blossom was a strangled mess.
My fist clenched "habbitly."
I didn't even know it when
Pain's manifest was me.

And when I saw my blossom's pain,
Fists gripping as a ghost,
I stooped to unpry painfully
So desperate to share close.

The grip has loosened,
Walls crash down
Around me all the time.
And my now blossom's big and bright
Sprung from the rubble's grime.

AFTERWORD

I am alive today because I fight. I am only able to have the joy and confidence I have now because I've decided to accept the free gift God has given me: the gift of His deep healing, His victorious living, His everlasting love.

If we could fight this thing by willpower alone, many of us would have given up our addictions a long time ago. Willpower is not the issue. There's something deeper, something spiritual, going on here. And whether you believe it or not, there are other forces out there fighting for your life. Fighting to distort your view of yourself, of beauty.

Why are you hiding? Why are you trying so hard to look the way you do? When you look in the mirror, do you look alive? Do your eyes sparkle with the life inside? Or do shadows of death and depression stare back at you?

And if you are one of the many who have become a slave to bulimia or anorexia, I pray you take a deeper look and understand the spiritual battle being waged against your soul. Your precious heart is dying. O beloved, you are worth so much more than that. There is so much more joy and freedom to be had, and your Daddy God wants you to experience His pleasures.

Know that there is a way out. You are not alone, precious child of the King. You are deeply loved. Know that I and many others are right there with you, fighting the thoughts every day and replacing them with the truth about our identities as His beloved creations.

I am more alive today than I have ever been. I am more confident, secure, and fulfilled today in this body than I ever was when I was a size X. And my prayer is that you, too, will find the truth in Christ: the truth that you are fearfully and wonderfully made, that the King of this universe is enthralled by your beauty. He chose every last detail of your body and character for a specific purpose. He is the only one who can give you the desires of your heart because He made you. He knows you better than you know yourself.

I still fight the monster. Every day I fight the lies that war against my soul. But the lies are much quieter now. And I have weapons to fight back. Each time I resist them, they get weaker—the armor covers more, and the truth about who I am is busy slaying their nasty suggestions.

The sword will accomplish the purpose for which it was sent. And the cool part is, I get to use it. O God, how I love kicking the devil's brains out.

> *The world needs you.*
> *Each and every one of you.*
> *Your heart is more than worth fighting for.*

Appendix A

Weapons for Identity

(This is the "confession sheet" I made specific to my battles)

THE King is enthralled by my beauty. I honor Him for He is my Lord (Psalm 45:11). All glorious, says the Lord, is My princess within her chamber. Her gown is interwoven with gold. In embroidered garments I am led to the King. My virgin companions follow me and are brought to You. I am led with joy and gladness as I enter Your palace, my King.

You, Jesus, are the Lord of my life. Apart from Jesus Christ I can do nothing. But in Jesus Christ I can do all things. I can resist temptation, for no temptation will overtake me that is not common to man. I see you, devil. I see that you tempt me with food to ease my anxiety, restlessness, boredom, loneliness, or dissatisfaction with myself. Well, guess what? You are a liar! I will not listen to your lies! I am open with my brothers. I do not live in isolation. I am not misunderstood.

I am a daughter of the King. I am beautiful, for the Creator of the universe knit me together in my mother's womb. I praise the Lord, for I am fearfully and wonderfully made. He chose every last detail of my body and character for a specific purpose. I am God's workmanship, created in Christ to do good works, which God has prepared in advance for me to do. I see myself as He sees me, according to His living Word. Therefore I am anxious for nothing! And I will not be mastered by anything! Food will never satisfy my desires. I find my identity, security, and fulfillment in Christ *alone!* Food for the stomach and the stomach for food, but God will destroy them both.

God gives me all the desires of my heart. His word is like honey to my lips. O Lord, when Your words came, I ate them; they were my joy and my heart's delight (Isaiah 15:16). So I say to you, devil, when I eat and drink, I am not just feasting for myself or to gratify the desires of my sinful nature. But whether I eat or drink or whatever I do, I do it all for the glory of God. This is my food: to do the will of the one who sent me and to complete His work. Every day I clothe myself with the Lord Jesus Christ. For my body is a temple of the Holy Spirit who is in me, whom I have received from God. I am not my own, nor am I yours, devil. I was bought at a price. Purchased by the blood of the Lamb, because He loves me and delights in me. I am *His!* Therefore, I honor God with my body.

Because the Spirit is in me, I have love, joy, peace, patience, kindness, goodness, faith, gentleness, and self control. I have self-control! Like a fortress whose walls are torn down is a person who lacks self-control. I am strong in the Lord! My eyes stay fixed on *Him.* No weapon formed against me shall prosper. My mind is being renewed by the Word of God. I pull down strongholds, I cast down imaginations, I bring every thought captive to the obedience of Christ. I am not a slave of sin. I'm a friend of God and a slave of righteousness. I am a new creation. Old things have passed away. All things have become new. I don't have to serve sin anymore. "Food gained by fraud tastes sweet, but I end up with a mouth full of gravel" (Proverbs 20:17). Stolen water is sweet, and food eaten in secret tastes delicious. But I know, Father, that the dead are there, that her guests are in the depths of the grave (Proverbs 9:17).

But I have risen from that grave, never to return. I was buried with Christ in baptism and am now walking in the newness of life, knowing that my old nature was crucified with Him so that I should no longer be a slave to sin. I reckon myself to be dead indeed to sin but alive in Christ Jesus my Lord. Sin has no dominion over me! I will not believe your works, devil! No longer will you oppress me! I will submit to God, for He is my Lord, my Father, my friend, and an ever-present help. He looks upon me with gladness. With me He is well-pleased. I am His heart's obsession, His only desire. I am the one He delights in always, no matter what.

Daddy, I praise You that Your love for me never changes! You are never disappointed, never distant, but always near with outstretched arms. You always long to hold me. You clothe me with peace. You long to unfold all Your blessings upon me. Therefore, because I am Yours, Lord, I will resist the devil, and he must flee! He is terrified of me, because I am more than a conqueror through Christ, who loves me.

I will strive always to keep my conscience clear before God and man (Act 24:16).

Lord, Your words are true. Your word is a mirror. It tells me who I am. As soon as I start believing it to be true, the devil no longer sees me. He sees You, Jesus. Thank You, Father, for Your Word. Today is a day of breakthrough! Today and forever, I am Yours. Use me, Father. For You are so worthy to be praised. Amen.

WEAPONS TO FIGHT THE ACCUSER

I clothe myself with compassion, kindness, humility, gentleness, and patience (Colossians 3:12). You have abundantly poured out on me the faith and love that are in Christ Jesus (1 Timothy 1:14). I bear with each other and devote myself to prayer (Colossians 4:2). I consider how I may spur one another on toward love and good deeds (Hebrews 10:17). A fool shows his annoyance at once, but a prudent man overlooks an insult (Proverbs 12:16). Pride only brings quarrels, but wisdom is found in those who take advice (Proverbs 13:10). I make every effort to live in peace with all men (Hebrews 12:14). The accuser of our brothers, who accuses them before our God day and night, has been hurled down (Revelation 12:10)! May the words of my mouth and the meditation of my heart be pleasing in Your sight (Psalm 19:14). Search me, O God, and know my heart; test me and know my thoughts. See if there is any offensive way in me, and lead me in the way everlasting (Psalm 139:23). I confess in the sight of God, who gives life to everything (1 Timothy 6:13).

I keep with the prophecies once made about me, so that by following them I may fight the good fight (1 Timothy 1:18). I do not neglect my gift, which was given through a prophetic message when the body of the elders laid their hands on me (1 Timothy 4:14). I do not let anyone look down on me because I am young, but I set an example for the believers in speech, in life, in love, in faith, and in purity (1 Timothy 4:11). In everything, I set an example by doing what is good. In my teaching, I show integrity, seriousness, and soundness of speech that cannot be condemned, so that those who oppose me may be ashamed because they have nothing bad to say about me (Titus 2:7). The Lord will rescue me from every evil attack and will bring me safely to His heavenly kingdom (2 Timothy 4:18).

I am active in sharing my faith so that I will have a full understanding of every good thing we have in Christ Jesus (Philemon 1:4). I fight the good fight of faith. I take hold of the eternal to which I was called when I made my confession in the presence of many witnesses (1 Timothy 6:12). I am strong in the grace that is in Christ Jesus, and the things I have heard You say, in the presence of many witnesses, I entrust to reliable men, who will also be qualified to teach others (2 Timothy 2:1-2). I hold firmly to the trustworthy message as it has been taught so that I can encourage others by sound doctrine and refute those who oppose it (Titus 1:19). Some will turn their ears away from the truth and turn aside to myths. But I will keep my head in all situations, endure hardship, do the work of an evangelist, discharge all the duties of my ministry (2 Timothy 4:4). Lord, You want all men to come to the knowledge of truth (1 Timothy 2:4). They will come to their senses and escape from the trap of the devil (2 Timothy 2:26). Your Scriptures are able to make us wise for salvation through faith in Christ Jesus.

All Scripture is God-breathed and is useful for teaching, rebuking, correcting, and training in righteousness so that the man of God may be thoroughly equipped for every good work (2 Timothy 3:15). God's Word will not return void but will fulfill the purpose for which it was sent. The Word of God is living and active. Sharper than any double-edged sword, it penetrates even to dividing soul and spirit, joints and marrow; it judges the thoughts and attitudes of the heart. Nothing in all creation is hidden from God's sight. Everything is uncovered and laid bare before the eyes of Him to whom we must give account (Hebrews 4:13).

I do not throw away my confidence, for it will be richly rewarded. I need to persevere so that when I have done the will of God, I will receive what he has promised. For in just a little while, He who is coming will come and will not delay (Hebrews 10:35-37). I throw off everything that hinders and the sin that so easily entangles, and I run with perseverance the race marked out for us. I fix my eyes on Jesus. I consider Him who endured such opposition from sinful men, so that I will not grow weary and lose heart (Hebrews 12:1-3).

WEAPONS FOR VICTORY
(SCRIPTURE PARAPHRASED)

I am not just an ordinary woman. I am a daughter of the Most High God. I am an heir of God and a joint heir with Jesus Christ; therefore, I am royalty (Galatians 4:7). I am a part of a chosen generation, a royal priesthood, a holy nation (1 Peter 2:9). So I fix my eyes not on what is seen, but on what is unseen. For what is seen is temporary, but what is unseen is eternal (2 Corinthians 4:18).

I'm not under guilt or condemnation (Romans 8:1). I refuse discouragement. There is therefore now no condemnation for those who are in Christ Jesus. Satan is a liar. I will not listen to his lies. I am open with my brothers.

I'm not ruled by my feelings. I'm not in bondage to my emotions. I'm not under the circumstances. I'm above the circumstances (Colossians 3:2). I am seated with Christ in the heavenly places (Ephesians 2:6).

His power is made perfect in my weakness (2 Corinthians 12:9). When the enemy comes in like a flood, the Spirit of the Lord will raise up a standard. I'm a part of that standard. My life is not just about me. We are the soldiers of the army of salvation that God is raising up to save this world. My calling and destiny are *huge!* I will not despise the days of small beginnings. We will reclaim that which the thief has stolen through tradition and ignorance (Zechariah 4:10). The earth and all who dwell here are the Lord's! (Psalms 24:1).

He said He would pour out His Spirit in these last days. Sons and daughters would prophesy, young men would see visions, and old men would dream dreams (Joel 2:28). I'm a part of this end-time vision for without it I will perish (Proverbs 29:18). For still the vision awaits its time, it hastens to an end, and it will not fail (Habakkuk 2:3). If it seems slow, I will wait for it. It will surely come. It will not delay. Therefore, I have a sense of destiny.

Jesus is restoring His church. It will be a triumphant church (Ephesians 5:27).I will kick in the gates of hell. I'm a part of this end-time move. God is at work in me to will and to work for His good pleasure (Philippians 2:13). The Lord will fulfill His purpose in me (Psalm 138:8).

I'm beginning today. I redeem the time. I'm not weighted down by the cares of this life. I cast all my cares upon the Lord (1 Peter 5:7). Whatever the task this day, I'll do it heartily, as if I was serving the Lord (Colossians 3:23).

I stir up the gifts within me. I step out in faith. I move in the supernatural. I set the captives free (Isaiah 61:1). I do not lack any spiritual gift as I eagerly wait for our Lord Jesus Christ to be revealed (1 Corinthians 1:7).

The Spirit of the Sovereign LORD is on me because the LORD has anointed me to preach good news to the poor. He has sent me to bind up the brokenhearted, to proclaim freedom for the captives and release from darkness for the prisoners, to proclaim the year of the LORD's favor, to comfort all who mourn, and provide for those who grieve in Zion. He has bestowed on me a crown of beauty instead of ashes, the oil of gladness instead of mourning, and a garment of praise instead of a spirit of despair. Therefore we will rejoice and give thanks to Him always! (Isaiah 61:1-4).

I'm a pioneer; I'm not a settler. I'm on the frontlines. I've counted the cost. I'll pay the price. I'm giving my utmost for His highest (Luke 14:26-33). I press on toward the goal of the prize of the high calling in Christ Jesus my Lord (Philippians 3:14). I'm out to change my generation. My ministry is maturing. I'm growing in grace. He who began a good work in me will bring it to completion in the day of my Lord Jesus (Philippians 1:6). Boldly, I can approach the throne of grace to receive mercy and grace for help in the time of need (Hebrews 4:16).

My life is taking on new responsibilities. I am anxious for nothing (Philippians 4:6). He will keep me in perfect peace, for my mind is stayed on Him (Isaiah 26:3). Therefore, I enter His rest (Hebrews 4:3). I have the mind of Christ. I have a sound mind (1 Corinthians 2:16). I have a spirit of love, power, and discipline (2 Timothy 1:7).

Whoever is born of God overcomes the world. This is the victory that overcomes the world, even my faith. Therefore I am an overcomer (1 John 5:4). I'm going from faith to faith, strength to strength, and glory to glory (2 Corinthians 3:18).

I am God's workmanship, created in Christ Jesus to do good works, which God has prepared in advance for me to do (Ephesians 2:10). I prepare my mind for action, and I set my hope fully on Christ Jesus (1 Peter 1:13). I am cleansed in the blood. No weapon formed against me shall prosper, and I shall refute every tongue rising against me in judgment (Isaiah 54:17). My mind is being renewed by the Word of God (Romans 12:2). I pull down strongholds, I cast down imaginations, I bring every thought captive to the obedience of Christ (2 Corinthians 10:5).

I am accepted in the beloved (Ephesians 1:6). If God be for me, who can be against me? (Romans 8:31). Greater is He who is in me than he who is in the world (1 John 4:4). Nothing can separate me from the love that is in Christ Jesus my Lord (Romans 8:39). As the Father loves Jesus, so does Jesus love me (John 17:23). I am the righteousness of God in Christ (2 Corinthians 5:21). The Word of God is near me, in my mouth, mind, and heart so that I can obey it (Deuteronomy 30:14).

I'm not a slave of sin; I'm a slave of righteousness (Romans 6:6, 19). I continue in the Word. I know the truth, and the truth has set me free. Because the Son sets me free, I am free indeed (John 8:32, 36).

God keeps me safe, and the evil one cannot not touch me (1 John 5:18).

I've been delivered out of the kingdom of darkness, and I'm now a part of the kingdom of God (Colossians 1:13). I'm born of God. I overcome the world. I am an overcomer! (1 John 5:4).

I don't have to serve sin anymore. Sin has no dominion over me. I do not believe the works of the devil. No longer will he oppress me (Romans 6:4). I get mad at the devil. I defeat him by the blood of the lamb, by the words of my testimony, and not by loving my life as to shrink from death (Revelation 12:11). I am strong in the Lord and the strength of His might (Joel 3:10).

I submit to God. I resist the devil, and he flees (James 4:7). No temptation will overtake me that is not common to man. God is faithful. He will not let me be tempted beyond my strength, but with the temptation will also provide a way of escape that I might be able to endure it (1 Corinthians 10:13). I hide Your Word in my heart, Lord, that I may not sin against You (Psalm 119:11). Your commandments aren't burdensome (1 John 5:3).

I stand fast in the liberty in which Christ has made me free (Galatians 5:1). Where the Spirit of the Lord is, there is freedom (2 Corinthians 3:17). The law of the Spirit of Life in Christ Jesus has set me free from the law of sin and death (Romans 8:2). I have life and life more abundantly (John 10:10). Your yoke is easy. Your burden is light (Matthew 11:28-30).

Christ always causes me to triumph. I reign as a queen in life through Christ Jesus (2 Corinthians 2:14). As a young woman, I am strong. The Word of God abides in me, and I have overcome the evil one (1 John 2:14). I cleanse myself from all dishonorable purposes and so become an instrument for noble purposes, made holy, useful to the Master and prepared to do any good work (2 Timothy 2:21). I am righteous by faith (Romans 5:1).

WEAPONS FOR BOLDNESS
(SCRIPTURE PARAPHRASED)

I give no opportunity to the devil (Ephesians 4:27). I give no place to fear in my life (1 John 4:18). Fear torments (Revelation 18:10). The fear of man brings a snare (Proverbs 29:25), but perfect love casts out all fear (1 John 4:18). I sought the Lord, and He heard my voice and delivered me from all fear (Psalm 34:4). God has not given me a spirit of fear, but a spirit of love, power, and a sound mind (2 Timothy 1:7).

In righteousness I am firmly established, so I'll be far from oppression. I will not fear or be in terror (Isaiah 54:14). It shall not come near me (Psalm 91:10). The Lord is my light and my salvation; whom shall I fear? The Lord is the strength of my life; of whom shall I be afraid (Psalm 27:1)? God is my refuge and strength, a very present help for time of trouble. Therefore, I will not fear (Psalm 46:1-2).

I have no fear of confrontation. I boldly confront the devil. If I were still trying to please men, I would not be a servant of Jesus Christ. But I am a servant of the Most High God (Galatians 1:10). I will not fear, for He is with me. I will not be dismayed, for He is my God. He will strengthen and help me with His victorious right hand (Isaiah 41:10).

I am not ashamed of the gospel, for it is the power of God for the salvation of everyone who believes (Romans 1:16). I'm a minister of reconciliation. I'm an ambassador for Jesus Christ. The anointing I've received abides in me through Jesus Christ, who loves me (2 Corinthians 5:18-20). I received power when the Holy Spirit came upon me to be His witness (Act 1:8).

His Word which comes out of my mouth will not return void, but will accomplish the purpose for which it was sent (Isaiah 55:11). I know my God. I am strong, and I will resist the enemy (Daniel 11:32). The kingdom of God suffers violence and those who take it, take it by force! (Matthew 11:12).

I have faith toward God. My faith is not in my faith, but in a living God who said He would never leave me or forsake me (Hebrews 13:5). Therefore I choose to walk by faith and not by sight (2 Corinthians 5:7). I trust in the Lord with all my heart, and I do not lean on my own understanding (Proverbs 3:5-6).

Many are the afflictions of the righteous, but the Lord delivers him out of them all. The righteous man falls seven times, but rises again. Champions don't give up. They get up (Proverbs 24:16). One thing I do, forgetting what lies behind and straining forward toward what lies ahead, I press on toward the goal of the prize of the high calling of Christ Jesus my Lord (Philippians 3:13-14).

I am righteous, therefore I'm as bold as a lion (Proverbs 28:1). He will never fail me nor forsake me; therefore, I can boldly say, the Lord is my helper, I'll not be afraid! What can man do to me? I am an effective evangelist. I minister life, and I win souls (Hebrews 13:5-6).

I am a good communicator. I am an effective and excellent teacher. I am strong. The Word of God abides in me, and I have overcome the evil one. I am an overcomer (1 John 4:17). I am complete in Him (Colossians 2:10).

MORE POEMS FROM
A BURNING HEART

October 1, 2007
More

How long? How long?
O God how long?
Must I live without You near?
I catch Your glimpses in the mirror,
Or as I dance, love without fear.
And I can see You in the trees,
Speaking Your love through perfect breeze.
And I feel You deep inside myself,
When I cry out or lie and melt
Under Your weight, You golden light,
But God, O, what I'd really like
Is You.
Not some feeling, not just grace,
Not all my thoughts floating through space.
O God show me!
Please reveal
Yourself to me,
a You more real.
I have to know You,
Have to see,
'Cause without You there is no me.

It's You I want, O Mystery,
It's You I want, it's You in me.
Jessica,
Let Me woo you, let Me sing
My love to you, my everything
My beautiful bride, please take My ring,
And here, My sweet one, take My wing.
Come fly with Me, away from here.
Let Me draw you, hold you dear.
O beloved, O sweet bride,
I am your Lover, by your side.
I won't leave you, I can't go.
Your beauty draws me, don't you know?
I am enthralled, you make Me dance.
My heart beats fast with just one glance.

So come to sleep, awaken love,
I rain My heart down from above.
I'll cover you, I am your love,
I'll cover you, the one I love.

December 6, 2007
Boldly I Come

Dad, here I am! I must have more! I'm bursting through. There is no door!
I come into the depths of You, plunge down into that deep rich hue
Of red and blue, and purple gold, the untamed colors of truths untold.
Unfold Your love, I'll put it on, and we can dance into Your dawn!

I want to wear Love like a robe, to sway with You inside Your glow,
To lie beneath the gemstone sky, the zillion sparkles of Your eyes.
Your eyes, deep pools of love and fire, that sing to me a healing choir
And I am captured by their song, where darkness knows it can't belong.
I watch it leaking like black oil, around me past the robes of royal,
And vanishing into the air as if the black was never there.

O, Dad, place on me a crown! Then wrap me up into Your gown.
Your hands are mercy, love and grace. I tremble as You love my face,
And touch me sweetly in this realm; I slow as senses overwhelm.
The air is sweet and thick and slow, Your movements trailing with love's
glow.

O my Daddy, Lover, King, O Mighty Ruler, Tender Wing,
Protector, Fortress, Playful One, I'm bare before You, heart's undone.
O search me now. I must be known. I must know You. I'm not my own.
I'm Yours. You said that I'm complete, inside of You where our depths meet.
And somehow I've completed You. I am Your fullness, we are new.

Glory Glory! All around, and Glory Glory at the sound
Of Your One Name, we glorify! And shout Your praises to the sky!

And Glory Glory! All around, and Glory Glory at the sound
Of Your One Name, Your Name renown. Inside Your glory, I am found.

February 14, 2008
I Say Come

I say come and You're here
I say love, You draw near,
I cry out and You hear,
God Your love knows no fear.

You saw and You've seen and yet You still redeem,
You come running to me and, yes, You set me free.

You saw and You've seen and yet You still redeem,
You come running to me and, yes, You set me free.

Again and again and again, God.
Again and again and again.

RECOMMENDED READING

I recommend reading an "eating-related" book in pair with a "bonding with God" book. That way you will begin to look outward and upward during healing instead of always inward.

Eating Related

1) *Life Without ED: How One Woman Declared Independence from Her Eating Disorder and How You Can Too* by Jenni Schaefer
2) *Bulimia: A Guide to Recovery* by Lindsey Hal
3) *Intuitive Eating* by Evelyn Tribole, M.S., R.D. and Elyse Resch, M.S., R.D., F.A.D.A
4) *Hope and Healing for Eating Disorders* by Gregory L. Jantz, Ph.D.

Bonding with God

1) *Passion for Jesus* by Mike Bickle
2) *Strengthen Yourself in the Lord* by Bill Johnson
3) *When Heaven Invades Earth* by Bill Johnson
4) *Purity: The New Moral Revolution* by Kris Vallotton

RECOMMENDED LISTENING

1) *Captured* by Alberto and Kim Rivera (Great "soaking" music)
2) *Forever and a Day* and *Crush* by Anthony Skinner
3) *Dark Yet Lovely* by Heather Clark
4) *Raw Sessions* and *In the Waiting* by Isa Couvertier
5) *The Song Inside the Sounds of Breaking Down* by John Mark McMillan
6) *Remember* and *Faith* by Jason Upton
7) *Here Is My Song* by Kim Walker
8) *Always on His Mind* and *Relentless* by Misty Edwards
9) *Constant* (Various Artists)
10) *Your Love Never Fails* (Various Artists)

RESOURCES TO FIND HELP

1) **NEDA (National Eating Disorders Association)** – The largest nonprofit in the U.S. dedicated to the elimination of eating disorders. Call NEDA's toll free, confidential Helpline Monday - Friday, 8:30 am to 4:30 pm PST: 1-800-931-2237. Nationwide listings. www.nationaleatingdisorders.org

2) **Center for Change** – A specialized treatment center where "hope is real." Utilizing the intuitive eating approach, Center for Change provides a nurturing environment for adolescent and adult woman with eating disorders. www.centerforchange.com

3) **Mercy Ministries of America** – A free-of-charge, biblically based program providing hope and healing to young women who are seeking freedom from life-controlling problems such as eating disorders. www.mercyministries.org

If you would like to order more copies of

Hungry

or contact Jessica,
please visit our website at
www.burningonebooks.com